WALKER SUN BOOKS

Aerodynamics

A SUN BOOK

Aerodynamics

JACQUES LACHNITT

Aeronautical Engineer

Translated by Janette C. Loder
and Charles G. Keil

A SUN BOOK

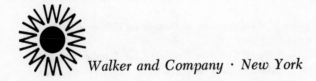 *Walker and Company · New York*

Preface

Of all the branches of physics, aerodynamics has taken the longest to develop. This stems from the nature of the science: the study of the phenomena associated with the movement of bodies relative to the air or the movement of the air relative to bodies. Until the middle of the last century, only preliminary research had been carried out in specific areas: the flow of fluids in pipes, the effect of moving air on buildings, the ballistics of projectiles, and so on.

Fortunately, the pioneers of aviation saw the need to understand the mechanics of flight before they could construct machines capable of carrying man aloft; and when, on December 17, 1903, the Wright brothers made the first controlled flight, it became even more apparent that the future of aerodynamics was almost unlimited.

In less than fifty years the collaboration of scientists, engineers and mathematicians led to flight at speeds in excess of sound. Today man can not only fly at supersonic speeds, but can make orbital flights around the earth and then re-enter the earth's atmosphere. Less exciting but perhaps even more significant, the advent of commercial aviation has meant that man can fly to any corner of the globe quickly and safely.

Furthermore, developments in aviation have led to progress in general scientific and engineering techniques that have benefited other fields of endeavor.

The time has come when a basic understanding of aerodynamics is essential to anyone who wishes to follow and understand the rapid advance of the sciences. The aim of this book is to provide a few basic elements in a realm that is continually growing due to the unceasing pressure for higher speeds that dominates the twentieth century.

May I conclude this preface by thanking P. Rebuffet, professor at the Ecole Nationale Supérieure de l'Aéronautique, and the Librairie Béranger for the figures that they have allowed me to reproduce from Professor Rebuffet's book *L'Aérodynamique experimentale,* one of the best works that has appeared on the subject.

J. L.

Contents

Aerodynamics

A SUN BOOK

1 / Historical

We must mention in passing man's earlier attempts to fly. These attempts were based on mythological beliefs and attempts to emulate the birds, rather than on even a remote idea of the importance of aerodynamics. The first ideas that were to prove useful in the formulation of a theory regarding the movement of bodies in fluids appeared in the sixteenth century, when the bases of mechanics were first laid down.

Galileo was the first man to understand the nature of the resistance of air; in studying the motion of a pendulum, he noticed that it gradually slowed down. He therefore sought to experimentally establish the relationship between air resistance and the velocity of the pendulum, as follows: Two identical pendula (made up of two spheres of the same weight and two suspension cords of equal length) were set in motion, with angular displacements of 10 degrees for the one and 160 degrees for the other. After a certain time interval the two pendula completed the same number of oscillations. Galileo therefore, thinking himself justified in assuming that the speeds of the two pendula were in the ratio of one to sixteen, deduced that air resistance was proportional to speed.

It was Newton who correctly asserted that air resistance is proportional to the square of a body's speed and linear dimensions, and to the density of the air. Furthermore, this great English scholar established the basic principle on which wind tunnels were later to be based: that the forces resulting from a body's immersion in a fluid are the same whether the body moves through the fluid at a certain speed or whether the fluid moves around a stationary body.

Moreover, the relationship between air resistance and speed (squared) was later shown to be inexact for high speeds, and ballistic experiments with shells showed that air resistance increased at a much higher rate than the speed squared.

Some years later the great French mathematician Jean Le Rond d'Alembert laid the foundations for modern mechanics, in a work entitled *Essai d'une nouvelle théorie de la résistance des fluides*. Unfortunately the book arrived at a rather misleading conclusion: that the resistance offered by a non-viscous fluid to a moving body is zero. This is the famous "d'Alembert's paradox," which we shall discuss again later.

Theoretical fluid mechanics made great strides in the

second half of the eighteenth century, assisted by developments in the closely allied field of hydrodynamics. This progress continued unabated through the nineteenth century. The names of the scientists, engineers, mathematicians and other scholars concerned with this progress are now identified with the particular rule or theory that bears their name. Bernoulli (1700–1782) formulated the famous equation concerning the flow of incompressible fluids: that along a streamline the sum of the dynamic pressure and the static pressure is constant. Leonhard Euler (1707–1783) took an intense interest in hydrodynamics and formulated certain fundamental laws of fluid mechanics. He established a theory (based on pressure effects) that linked fluid resistance to the movement of bodies. Pierre Simon de Laplace (1749–1827) contributed an exact formula for the speed of propagation of sound in air: he showed that it is proportional to the square root of the absolute temperature. This formula corrected the first evaluation given by Newton, which was 15 per cent lower than that reached in experiments.

During the course of the nineteenth century, also, the development of the artillery projectile stimulated the study of supersonic phenomena. Firing tests were carried out at speeds up to 5,000 ft./second. It was during such tests that the Austrian physicist Ernst Mach discovered the shock waves that accompany bodies traveling at supersonic speeds. Mach suggested a strioscopic method of observing irregularities in supersonic flow that is still in use today.

About this time the idea of building an aircraft became firmly rooted. The first models produced owed much to the study of bird flight. Sir George Cayley had already shown that the key to producing lift was the shape of the wing profile. Cayley also designed the first wing profile based on aerodynamic considerations (supposedly, on the transverse section of the trout).

Also at about this time, the first aerodynamic testing systems were set up. In England Francis H. Wenham in 1871, and then Phillips in 1891, built wind tunnels; they were followed by Nikolai E. Joukowski in Russia, and C. E. A. Rateau and Gustave Eiffel in France. Eiffel is generally acknowledged to have been the first to understand and formulate the basic techniques of wind-tunnel testing; indeed many of his techniques are still used. He built his famous tower in 1910 in order to measure the air resistance of flat plates. From that time on, the development of aerodynamics progressed apace with the construction of aircraft, advances in aerodynamics providing data that made possible performance improvements in aircraft. The German aerodynamicist Ludwig Prandtl provided an exact theory of wing lift and an explanation of the behavior of air flow (1920). Prandtl also developed the concept of the boundary layer—a branch of aerodynamics subsequently pursued with great success by Theodore von Karman. Prandtl and the Englishman Glauert established the effects of the compressibility of air at high speeds (1928). Then the first theory of supersonic flow around a wing was given—by Ackerett—while an improved method was contributed by Adolf Büsemann (1935).

During World War II the first characteristics of flight

in the transonic region were manifested by some propeller-driven fighter aircraft—like Britain's Supermarine Spitfire —in the course of steep or vertical dives. These phenomena were of immediate importance for the first aircraft powered by turbojet engines, and from 1945 on, a vast program of wind-tunnel testing to evaluate flow characteristics at Mach 1 and above was carried out. The result has been complete understanding of the aerodynamic behavior of aircraft flying at about the speed of sound, and attainment of today's supersonic speeds.

The development of special missiles—some of which now reach speeds of thousands of miles an hour—has contributed further knowledge regarding the high Mach number range. For the dominant feature of aerodynamics, compared with other physical sciences, is that it is always in a state of evolution, and progresses with the increase in speed and general performance of aircraft.

2 / General Phenomena

Fluid Flow: Generalities

A perfect fluid—one that is neither viscous nor compressible —is an ideal, although it would be of considerable use in developing an initial mathematical theory. However, the phenomena of compressibility do not become manifest until flow speeds approaching the local speed of sound, so that it is customary to ignore this effect and to take viscosity into account only at lower speeds.

Let us begin by seeing how the speed of sound affects fluid mechanics; this will permit us to break flow down into different categories. If we exert on a volume of fluid a small displacement, it gives rise to a variation in pressure that spreads through the fluid at a finite speed—in fact, the speed of sound, because sounds are nothing more than pressure changes. The speed of sound depends on the nature and physical state of the fluid, but not on the nature of the disturbance that causes the pressure fluctuation. The speed is proportional to the square root of the temperature and can be expressed by the formula $a = 20.1 \sqrt{T}$. In the standard atmosphere at ground level $a = 760$ m.p.h., at 36,000 feet, $a = 660$ m.p.h. Between these two values the variation is linear.

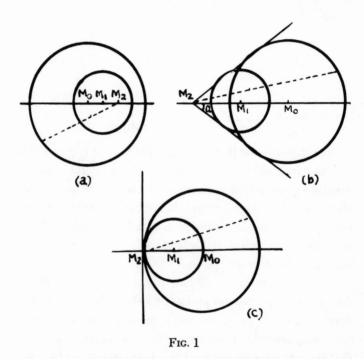

Fig. 1

Let us now consider a point M in a fluid moving at speed V. This source emits continual disturbances in the form of spherical wave fronts centered on the disturbance. Compared with the moving source, the speed of these disturbances is $a - V$ in the direction of the source movement and $a + V$ in the opposite direction. If V is lower than a, the disturbance travels faster than the source, and the spheres centered on the moving source extend out into space, as shown in Figure 1(a). If V is higher than a, the source travels at a higher speed than the disturbance, and the spherical wave fronts remain perpetually inscribed in a cone at the apex of which is the source. The angle subtended by this cone a is given by $\sin a = (a/V)$, as shown in Figure 1(b). The flow is supersonic. The conic envelope is called the *Mach wave*, after Ernst Mach, who photographed these phenomena in 1887. The boundaries of this cone are the *Mach lines*. Finally, we define the *Mach number* as $M = V/a$, i.e. the ratio of the speed of a body to the speed of sound in a given fluid.

In the particular case where $V = a$, the conical envelope is reduced to a plane normal to the direction of the movement and passing through the source. The spheres all remain tangent to this plane, as shown in Figure 1(c).

General Relationships in Fluid Flow

Let us begin by considering a small element of fluid that is moving, and examine its equilibrium. On any of its faces this parallelepiped of fluid exerts a force that can be split into two components: a pressure force normal to the element; and a viscous force tangential to the element. A perfect fluid is often defined as one in which the viscous forces are zero.

In a real fluid the viscous force is given by the expression:

$$dF_T = \mu \ \frac{\delta V}{\delta n} \ ds$$

where μ is the coefficient of viscosity, ds is the element of fluid on which the force dF_T is exerted, and $\delta V/\delta n$ is the velocity gradient normal to the surface element.

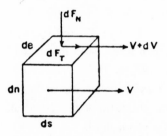

FIG. 2

Returning to the elementary parallelepiped shown in Figure 2, we can state that the sum of the forces to which the element is subjected is zero. These forces are the weight (ρq ds dn de, where ρ is the density of the fluid), the pressure forces on each face; and the inertia forces.

The equation of equilibrium, which we will not derive here, can be written:

$$qdz + (dp/\rho) + VdV = 0$$

This is the generalized form of Bernoulli's equation.

In the case of an incompressible fluid, the density is everywhere constant, and the preceding equation can therefore be integrated to give:

$$qz + (p/\rho) + \tfrac{1}{2}V^2 = \text{constant}$$

If the first or volumetric term (qz) is neglected, as for all practical aerodynamic problems, an even simpler form of the equation is obtained:

$$p + \tfrac{1}{2}\rho V^2 = \text{constant}$$

The term $\tfrac{1}{2}\rho V^2$ is encountered frequently in aerodynamics, and is known as the *dynamic pressure*, while the two terms together are known as the *total pressure*. Bernoulli's theorem is expressed by saying that the total pressure along a streamline in a perfect incompressible fluid remains constant.

In the case of a compressible fluid, ρ is no longer constant, and it is necessary therefore to establish a relationship between pressure and density. If it is assumed that the relationship is isentropic, then we can state that:

$$p/\rho^\gamma = \text{constant}$$

It is now possible to integrate Bernoulli's equation, and this gives:

$$\tfrac{1}{2}V^2 + \frac{\gamma}{\gamma - 1}\frac{p}{\rho} = \text{constant}$$

which is sometimes called the *St-Venant equation.*

It will be recalled that γ is the ratio between the specific heat of air at constant pressure and that at constant volume.

Types of Flow with Shock Waves

Since the end of the last century, ballistics experts, in the course of studying the flight of shells and bullets, have demonstrated the existence of shock waves in the vicinity of bodies moving at speeds faster than sound. These shock waves constitute discontinuities in the flow, across which the speed, pressure, density and temperature of the air undergo sudden changes.

Shock waves can be considered under two basic headings: the *normal shock,* across which (as its name suggests) the flow of air is normal to the shock, and where the velocity of the air changes from supersonic ahead of the shock to subsonic after it; and the *oblique shock,* in which the direction of flow deviates from the undisturbed flow direction after the air has passed through the shock. The velocity component parallel to the shock wave remains constant on each side of the shock wave.

Now let us consider the case of a flow in a corner, as shown in Figure 3. Initially, the free-stream Mach number M_0 ahead of the corner is below 1, but once M_0 exceeds 1, a curved shock wave forms just ahead of the corner, which is said to be a *detached shock.* If the Mach number M_0 increases further, the curvature of the shock wave decreases, and for a certain value M_0' the shock wave becomes straight and oblique and attached to the vertex of the angle at the corner.

For each value of the angle Φ there is a corresponding Mach number M_0' at which the shock wave ceases to become detached and curved and becomes attached and straight. This value of M_0' increases as the value of the angle Φ increases. Inversely, for a given Mach number there exists a maximum value of the angle beyond which the shock wave becomes detached and curved.

The characteristics of the air behind the shock wave

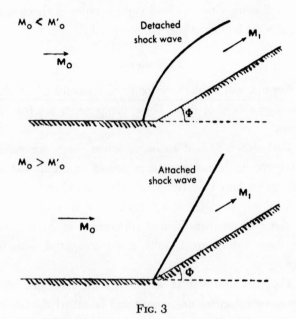

FIG. 3

(which are designated by the index $_1$) are related to the properties of the air in front of the shock wave (denoted by the index ^{0}) as follows:

$$p_1 > p_0$$
$$l_1 > l_0$$
$$\rho_1 > \rho_0$$
$$M_1 < M_0$$

In general terms, it can be said that across a shock wave the air is subjected to a transformation in which the kinetic energy of the molecules is converted into pressure energy and heat energy, which raises its temperature. We shall see in the following chapters how various types of shock waves form around bodies at supersonic speeds.

Turbulence

Let u, v and w be the velocity components of a particle of fluid in a field of flow. These components are functions of time.

Turbulence is said to occur when there are random fluctuations in the component velocities superimposed on a steady mean flow velocity. Thus where u', v' and w' repre-

$$u = \bar{u} + u'; \quad v = \bar{v} + v'; \quad w = \bar{w} + w'$$

sent the random disturbances superimposed on the mean flow; these values are usually small compared with $\bar{u}$, $\bar{v}$ and $\bar{w}$.

The time interval at which the mean values of the component velocities are considered is called the *scale of turbulence*. This factor varies considerably depending on the type of phenomena. For example, the study of meteorology is concerned with the huge air masses of the earth's atmosphere, and the scale of turbulence here might be about an hour. For a pilot concerned with wind fluctuations likely to affect his flight, the factor may be only a few minutes, whereas for the aerodynamicist this period is reduced to fractions of a second.

The turbulent condition of fluid flow was first brought to light by Osborne Reynolds in 1883, following a series of experiments on the flow of water in tubes.

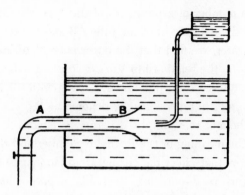

A horizontal glass tube AB is installed in the side of a trough of water, as shown in Figure 4; the end of the tube has a splayed mouth opposite which is fixed another very fine tube. Colored liquid flows out from this fine tube from a reservoir mounted above the water trough. The external end of the tube AB contains a tap that can be operated to vary the rate of discharge of the water from the trough.

If the tap is opened slightly, water is discharged at a slow rate from the trough, and the colored liquid from the fine tube flows into the wider tube AB parallel to the axis of the tube; this is called *laminar flow*.

If the tap is now opened further, the rate of water discharge increases, and the flow of colored liquid from the thin tube remains steady or laminar for a short distance, then suddenly becomes disturbed and mixes with the water; this is called *turbulent flow*.

If a number of experiments of this type are carried out, varying the diameter d of the tube AB and the temperature of the water, we find that the occurrence of turbulent flow depends on the relationship Vd/ν = constant, where ν is the kinematic viscosity of the water. This quantity is known as the *Reynolds number*—usually denoted as R.

Although this simple experiment effectively demonstrates the meaning of the Reynolds number and the principal factors that affect the change from laminar to turbulent flow, workers duplicating Reynolds' experiments showed that the value of R, for which flow changed from laminar to turbulent flow, also depended on the experimental conditions, such as the distance of the mouth of the fine tube from the mouth of the tube AB.

As we shall see, this change to turbulent flow is extremely important in aerodynamics, affecting as it does the behavior of bodies (particularly aircraft surfaces) that are subjected to it. In wind-tunnel testing, measures are generally taken to avoid the possibility of the air being turbulent in the actual test section. To measure turbulence a sensitive instrument capable of measuring the change from laminar to turbulent flow—the hot wire anemometer—is used; it is described in a later chapter.

The Boundary Layer

Experiment has shown that when a body is immersed in a moving fluid, whether air or water, the molecules of fluid immediately adjacent to that body adhere to it; the velocity of these surface molecules is therefore zero. As one moves out normally to the partition wall, the velocity of the molecules encountered gradually increases, until eventually, at some distance from the surface, the velocity of the molecules of the fluid is the same as that of the undisturbed fluid ahead of the body. The comparatively thin layer of fluid in which the velocity increases from zero to the free-stream value is called the *boundary layer*. The importance of this layer is that it consists of an infinite number of layers of fluid, each with a velocity different from the adjacent layer, so that important friction or viscous forces arise. These viscous forces, depending as they do on the characteristics of the boundary layer, determine the value of the surface friction drag of the whole body.

We have seen that the velocity of the fluid adjacent to the body surface changes gradually from zero to the velocity of the free stream. But as it is virtually impossible to fix the point at which the flow reverts to the free-stream velocity, it is customary to define this position (which is the edge of the boundary layer) by saying that it occurs where the velocity is 0.99 that of the free stream.

Now let us consider a horizontal flat plate immersed in a fluid whose condition is laminar. The speed u, parallel to the flow, is measured at two points on the plate measured in the horizontal direction x as shown in Figure 5. The velocity u is then measured over a range of vertical distances from the surface of the plate y, also as shown in Figure 5, so that velocity profiles for the boundary layer at points 1

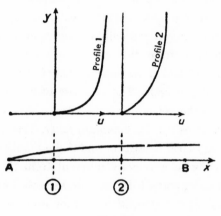

Fɪɢ. 5

and 2 can be plotted. It can be seen from the plots of these two profiles that the boundary layer grows from zero thickness at the nose of the plate to a maximum value at the down-stream end, and that the rate at which the velocity is changing to that of the free-stream velocity varies for different points along the plate. The velocity u diminishes in the direction of the flow because the kinetic energy of the fluid is being used to overcome the friction forces on the plate.

The kinetic energy is thus converted to heat energy, so that the surface of the plate is heated to a temperature higher than that of the free-stream fluid. As a result of progressive retardation of the fluid adjacent to the body, the thickness of the boundary layer increases from the upstream end of the plate to the downstream end. The boundary layer thickness, denoted by the symbol δ, is given by the expression:

$$\delta = 4.92 \sqrt{\nu x / u_0}$$

if the flow within the boundary layer is laminar. In this expression u_0 denotes the free-stream velocity of the fluid, and ν is once again the kinematic viscosity of the fluid. The thickness of the laminar boundary layer is directly proportional to the square root of the distance from the leading edge or upstream edge of the plate. The kinematic viscosity is in fact the ratio of the coefficient of absolute viscosity to the fluid density. Theoretical studies carried out by a number of workers—in particular Blausius—have shown that the velocity profile of the boundary layer at any particular value of u is independent of the value of x at the section considered.

We have already seen that when the Reynolds number of fluid flow reaches a certain value the character of the flow changes from laminar to turbulent, and that this effect is repeated in the boundary layer. In the classical Reynolds number experiment described above, the diameter of the tube was considered to be the vital dimension, whereas for the boundary layer the distance x from the leading edge is the important dimension. The boundary layer Reynolds number is thus given by the expression:

$$R_x = \frac{ux}{\nu}$$

In the turbulent boundary layer, we again meet the condition of uniform flow upon which is superimposed the random disturbances. This turbulent flow gives rise to higher shear forces and a consequent increase in the energy dissipation. In other words, the frictional forces in the turbulent boundary layer are much higher than those encountered in the laminar boundary layer, and the turbulent boundary layer therefore produces a greater drag force on the plate. (We might mention here that the turbulent boundary layer is much more robust than the laminar boundary layer.)

Although the transition from laminar to turbulent flow takes place once the critical Reynolds number has been exceeded, it is worth noting that there still exists within the turbulent boundary layer—and immediately adjacent to the wall of the body or plate to which the boundary layer is attached—a narrow region of fluid in which the flow is laminar. This is known as the *laminar sub-layer.*

The turbulent boundary layer profile consists of a linear relationship between the local velocity u and the distance y, measured vertical to the surface, over the lower values of y for which the laminar sub-layer is effective, followed by a relationship of the form $u = Ky^{1/7}$ for the turbulent region.

$$\delta = 0.37x(R_x^{-0.2})$$

Comparing this equation with that given above for the laminar boundary layer, we see that the rate of growth of the thickness of the turbulent boundary layer is higher than that for the laminar, since the thickness is directly proportional to the distance x to the power 0.8 compared with the power 0.5 for the laminar boundary layer.

In practice, the boundary layer seldom remains laminar throughout the whole length of a body, since the free-stream

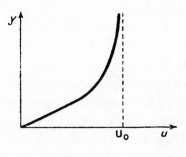

FIG. 6

air itself contains flow irregularities that tend to make the laminar layer unstable; also, surface roughness of the body creates disturbances that hasten the transition to turbulent flow. So far we have discussed the characteristics of the boundary layer on a flat plate, but in fact these remain generally true also for curved surfaces, such as aircraft wings, tail planes and fins. With the latter, the position of the transition point depends on the pressure gradient along the surface. On a smooth plane surface—such as the flat plate we considered initially—the pressure will remain constant throughout the length (i.e. the pressure gradient is zero), and the critical Reynolds number at which boundary-layer flow changes from laminar to turbulent will have a value of about 6×10^6. Although we customarily use the expression *transition point* for the change-over, it should be appreciated that it is more accurate to regard this as a transition zone, the size of which depends on the type of flow.

The transition point on a body can be found experimentally by a number of methods. One of these consists of plotting the velocity profile in the boundary layer at various points along the length of the body, and then noting at which section the profile is turbulent. The velocity profile is measured by means of a hot wire anemometer.

Visual methods may also be used, such as coating the surface with a volatile fluid; the evaporation of the fluid will be much quicker in the turbulent region and it will thus be possible to see where transition takes place. Another method (rarely used in practice) is acoustical; it involves detecting the higher noise level in the turbulent boundary layer, and thus again determining the transition point.

To return to the factors that influence the position of the transition point: We have already noted that initial disturbances in the free-stream flow advance the change-over to turbulent flow. However, the irregularities in the surface of the body have a more noticeable effect. If a surface irregularity is entirely submerged in the boundary layer, its effect on the rate of transition is almost negligible. On the other hand, if such an irregularity extends above the thickness of the laminar boundary layer, it has a marked effect on the early transition to turbulent flow.

It is possible to delay the transition by means of a porous wall through which boundary-layer air is sucked. This reduces the thickness of the boundary layer and stabilizes it in such a way that it remains laminar.

The position of the transition point has an important effect on the skin-friction drag of the body. If we consider the simplest aerodynamic body—a flat plate—with a length l and a width b, the skin-friction force or resistance of the plate in a stream of air having a velocity V and a density ρ is given by the expression:

$$F = \tfrac{1}{2} C_{xf} \rho V^2 l b$$

where C_{xf} is the coefficient of friction. The value of this coefficient is related directly to the Reynolds number and the nature of the flow, and since the skin-friction drag of the turbulent boundary layer is higher than that of the laminar layer (see Figure 7), in general it is desirable to insure that the boundary layer over the surfaces of an air-craft is laminar, so that drag is kept to a minimum. How-ever, this state of affairs is seldom achieved, because as the Reynolds number of the aircraft increases (as also the value of the Reynolds number of the various surfaces), the tran-sition point moves farther forward, and in the case of the aircraft's wings, flow may be laminar only over the first 10 per cent of the chord.

Manufacturing techniques exert an important influence on the transition point: raised rivetheads or similar excres-cences may cause the boundary layer to be almost wholly turbulent and thus produce high skin-friction drag forces, which affect the aircraft's performance adversely.

Separation

The viscous forces responsible for the boundary layer are also responsible for *separation*. This occurs when the external pressure gradient affects the velocity profile in the boundary layer to the extent that the direction of the flow near the surface, instead of being zero, has a negative value.

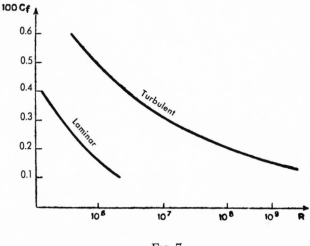

FIG. 7

In other words, there is reverse flow in the boundary layer near the surface. This causes the boundary layer to detach from the surface of the body, and it is then said to separate.

The position of the point of separation depends critically on the nature of this external pressure gradient, and whereas a turbulent boundary layer, with its robust mixing action, is able to withstand strong adverse pressure gradients, the more sensitive laminar boundary layer is less able to do so. Although the detached or separated boundary layer may subsequently reattach itself to the surface, it inevitably produces a thick wake at the rear of the body, which is in turn responsible for creating a high drag force.

We can see, therefore, that although the drag of a turbulent boundary layer is higher than that of the laminar boundary layer, the ability of the turbulent layer to resist separation with its attendant high wake drag can make it desirable to have a turbulent boundary layer under certain conditions. A golf ball provides a simple example. If it were perfectly smooth, the laminar boundary layer would detach from the surface closer to the front of the ball, due to the adverse pressure gradient. But the use of dimples or small holes causes the boundary layer to become turbulent at an early point; separation is thereby delayed and the width of the wake reduced. This means that the dimpled golf ball has a lower total drag level than its smoother counterpart, and therefore with the same applied force, will travel farther.

At high speeds the existence of a shock wave, with its associated rapid pressure change, will precipitate separation of the boundary layer.

Separation can be delayed or suppressed by the reduction of the external pressure gradient or by energizing the boundary layer. The latter process can be achieved by blowing air through slits or holes in the surface to revitalize the air in the boundary layer, and thus delay separation (or if it has already taken place, cause reattachment).

Aerodynamic Forces

Any body immersed in a moving fluid is submitted to viscous forces that act tangentially to the body on the one hand, and to normal pressure forces on the other.

The combination of these forces, as for any other system of forces, can be reduced to a resultant force R acting at a certain point, and an accompanying moment M. The point chosen for this reduction is usually the center of gravity of the body under consideration.

The axes of coordinates used for analysis of the force system acting on an aircraft can be based on either: (1) the direction of the airstream (Ox, Oy and Oz); or (2) the

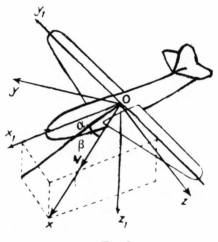

FIG. 8

plane of the aircraft (Ox$_1$, Oy$_1$ and Oz$_1$). Figure 8 shows the respective positions of the sets of axes of these coordinate systems. Their positions in space relative to each other are defined by two angles of considerable importance in aerodynamics: the incidence a, which is the angle between the planes x$_1$Oy$_1$, and xOy$_1$; and the sideslip β, which is the angle between the planes x$_1$Oz$_1$ and xOz$_1$.

Now let us adopt the coordinate axes related to the free-stream flow direction of the wind axes. The resultant force R then has three components:

R_x – the drag force.

R_y – the crosswind force.

R_z – the lift force.

In the same way, for the resulting moment M there are three components:

M_x – the rolling moment.

M_y – the pitching moment (sometimes referred to simply as M).

M_z – the yawing moment.

These forces can be non-dimensionalized by dividing by the factor $\frac{1}{2}\rho V^2 S$—as the moments can be non-dimensionalized by dividing by the factor $\frac{1}{2}\rho V^2 Sc$—where

ρ = air density

S = total wing area

c = mean wing chord

This gives for the forces the following coefficients:

C_x – drag coefficient (more commonly known as C_D).

C_y – drift coefficient.

C_z – lift coefficient (more commonly known as C_L).

and for the moment coefficients:

C_l – rolling moment coefficient.

C_m – pitching moment coefficient.

C_n – yawing moment coefficient.

3 / The Aerodynamics of Stream-
lined Bodies: The Wing At
Low Speeds

The Sphere

Some of the first experimental aerodynamic measurements on spheres were carried out by Eiffel, in 1911. His work led to a value for the drag coefficient of the sphere C_D of 0.176 —whereas later calculations by other workers gave a value of 0.44. The two different values can be explained by reference to the influence of the Reynolds number. If a large number of experiments are carried out with spheres of varying diameter d and with various speeds V, so that the Reynolds number (Vd/v) varies over a wide range, and the drag coefficient of the sphere C_D is obtained at the various Reynolds numbers, then a plot can be made of the relationship between C_D and the Reynolds number. This is shown

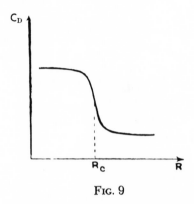

FIG. 9

in Figure 9. The curve of the relationship shows that there are two essentially different types of flow around the sphere. These are the direct result of the phenomena of separation, and a manifestation of the effect already described for the golf ball. For the upper horizontal part of the graph of Figure 9, the boundary layer is laminar, and separation occurs at the position shown by the dotted line in the left-hand figure of Figure 10.

As the Reynolds number increases, the boundary layer becomes turbulent; and because it is now more robust, it is able to withstand the effect of the adverse pressure gradient. Separation takes place at a much later position on the sphere (as shown in the right-hand figure of Figure 10), and the drag coefficient falls to the value shown by the approximately straight horizontal part of the curve in Figure 9. The reason for this decrease in the value of the

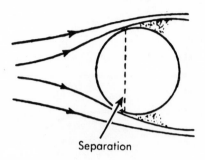

Separation

FIG. 10

drag coefficient as the Reynolds number increases is that the wake drag is much higher when the laminar boundary layer separates than it is for separation of the turbulent boundary layer at the point closer to the rear of the sphere. The pressure distribution on the sphere is very different in the two cases.

The Reynolds number at which this sudden change in drag coefficient occurs is referred to as the *critical Reynolds number,* and the value is closely dependent on the degree of turbulence in the free stream. For this reason the sphere has been used for some time as a measure of the degree of turbulence in wind-tunnel flow.

As the Mach number increases, the value of the critical Reynolds number increases considerably, so that above $M = 0.8$, C_D remains practically constant whatever the Reynolds number.

The Cylinder

When a cylinder is immersed in a perfect fluid traveling at a uniform speed V_0, the flow characteristics in any plane at right angles along the cylinder is the same, and furthermore is symmetrical (as shown in Figure 11) both in

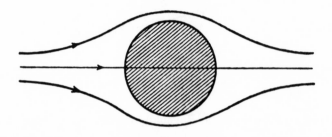

Fig. 11

the direction of flow and at right angles to it. This means that both the flow pattern and the pressure distribution around the sphere are doubly symmetrical, so that the resultant of all the pressures acting on the sphere is zero. This is the first example of the well-known d'Alembert's paradox.

We now introduce the concept of circulation. The actual flow (as opposed to that in a perfect fluid) over any body can in general be considered as a combination of translational and circulating flow. This circulation may be first considered as a rotation of the cylinder itself at constant speed. The effect of this circulation added to the translational flow of the perfect fluid shown in Figure 11, plus the effect of viscosity or friction forces (which do not, of course, exist in the perfect fluid) give rise to the flow pattern about the cylinder shown in Figure 12. The stag-

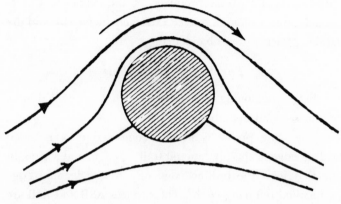

Fɪɢ. 12

nation point—i.e. the point at which fluid impinges normal to the body surface and the flow is brought to rest instantaneously—is, in the case of the flow of a perfect fluid around a cylinder, in the plane of symmetry (Figure 11). With clockwise circulation, the two stagnation points move downward, for a flow direction from left to right, as shown in Figure 12.

Whereas the resultant force on a cylinder in a perfect fluid is zero, a net force is exerted on a cylinder rotating in a viscous fluid. The first discovery of this force is attributed to Heinrich Gustav Magnus, and it is therefore referred to as the *Magnus effect*. At one time serious consideration was given to using this property of a revolving cylinder for propelling boats; and in fact a number of ships were constructed on this basis. They had vertical cylinders that were rotated by motors, and the propulsive force was provided by the Magnus effect force produced by the cylinders. Unfortunately, this technique proved extremely inefficient, and the various projects were abandoned.

The Wing: Definitions

Before beginning a study of the wing, we will discuss certain relevant definitions.

The wing profile is usually composed of a rounded leading edge, a sharply tapered trailing edge, and a straight line that joins the trailing edge (B) to the leading edge (A), called the *wing chord*. The surfaces ASB and AIB are known simply as the upper and lower surfaces (Figure 13).

A wing profile or aerofoil is generally defined by the position of its centerline (the line joining the mid-points of the lines perpendicular to the chord) and by the relationship between the x and y coordinates.

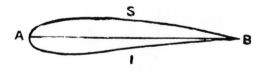

Fig. 13

To define completely the wing profile or aerofoil shape, four quantities are needed:

1. The camber, which is the curvature of the centerline of the aerofoil.

2. The position of the maximum ordinate or maximum thickness of the aerofoil, expressed in per cent chord.

3. The thickness ratio, which is the ratio between the maximum thickness and the chord.

4. The radius of the leading edge.

If we now consider a wing having a surface area S and a span 2b, we can define another important term—the *aspect ratio*. This is expressed in the form:

$$\lambda = 4b^2/S$$

The simplest planform is rectangular in shape, i.e. the points situated at x per cent of the chord on all the profiles are positioned on the same line perpendicular to the axis of symmetry. A wing is said to be swept when the corresponding points on each profile at the same per cent chord (x) are not on the same perpendicular to the axis of symmetry. Wing sweep is usually defined as the angle between a perpendicular to the fuselage axis of symmetry and either the wing leading edge or the quarter chord line.

Finally, wing taper is defined as the ratio between the wing root chord and the wing tip chord.

The Wing of Infinite Span in Incompressible Flow

The flow around aerofoils of certain shapes may be deduced theoretically by means of a mathematical process called *conformal transformation*. The process begins with a knowledge of the flow around a cylinder in two-dimensional incompressible flow.

In 1905 Joukowski calculated the resultant force on an aerofoil in a perfect, incompressible fluid, and obtained the result:

$$R = -\rho_0 V_0 \Gamma L$$

where V_0 is the velocity of the free-stream air, L is the length of the wing element with regard to the span, and Γ is the circulation, i.e. the integral $\left(\int V \cos \theta \, ds \right)$ of the velocity component around the contour of the wing profile.

We now define the dimensionless lift coefficient C_L so that:

$$R = \tfrac{1}{2}\rho_0 V_0^2 C_L S$$

where S again represents the surface area of the wing element under consideration.

The above equations allow us to write that

$$C_L = 2k_a$$

The coefficient k depends on the aerofoil characteristics, and generally has a value in the neighborhood of π (3.142), so that we can write:

$$C_L = 2\pi a$$

Real flow around a wing of infinite span can be studied by placing the wing in a wind-tunnel test section so that the two ends of the wing are built into the sides of the tunnel, thus removing the end effects due to a wing of finite span.

At low incidences the actual flow is very close to that predicted by the theory, but the maximum lift is much lower than that predicted. The rate of change of the lift coefficient with incidence $dC_L/d\alpha$ is slightly lower than that given by the theory (about 85 per cent).

We have seen that in a perfect fluid the resultant force of the fluid on the aerofoil was normal in the free-stream direction, so that there was no drag force. This is d'Alembert's paradox. In a real fluid the friction forces and the pressure distribution affecting the aerofoil produce a drag force D, and the drag coefficient is expressed in the form:

$$C_D = D/\tfrac{1}{2}\rho V^2 S$$

The Wing of Finite Span

An extensive theory of finite wings has been propounded by Prandtl. For a wing of infinite span the flow pattern is identical at any particular point along the span. When the span is finite, there is a tip effect, resulting from the movement of air from the lower to the upper surface. Because the pressure on the upper surface of the wing is negative (i.e. there is a lift-producing suction pressure), the air attempts to flow so that the pressures on the lower and upper surfaces become equal. The result is that the direction of the air flow over the wing is deflected in such a way that air passing over the upper surface is deflected toward the center of the wing span (toward the fuselage in an actual aircraft) and air passing over the lower surface is deflected toward the wing tip. This means that the directions of the upper and lower surface flows are different when the two streams meet at the wing trailing edge. This effect produces a vortex at each point M on the trailing

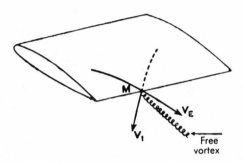

FIG. 14

edge, as shown in Figure 14; Prandtl called these *free vortices*. The vortices are parallel to the free-stream flow direction, and their strength depends on the variation of the pressure distribution over the upper and lower surfaces from wing root to wing tip. The wing can be·replaced by a bound vortex parallel to the span, and this in turn can be replaced by an infinite number of vortices coinciding with the number of free vortices at the trailing edge. In a plan view we can see that we have built up a model of vortices that effectively replace the wing as shown in Figure 15.

This free vortex sheet produces a downward velocity at each point on the wing, called the *downwash of induced downwash* (denoted by the symbol w). When this downwash velocity is combined with the free-stream velocity V_0 (as in Figure 16) to give the resultant effective velocity V, this acts at an angle to the free-stream velocity a_i, called the

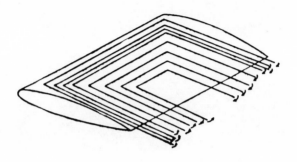

Fig. 15

induced incidence. The resultant of the aerodynamic forces, which acts at right angles to the resultant effective velocity V, now has a component in the direction of the free-stream velocity, which is the induced drag D_i.

Prandtl showed that the induced drag for a wing has a minimum value when the wing has elliptic loading—in other words, when the distribution of the circulation over the span takes the form:

$$\Gamma = \Gamma_0 \sqrt{1 - (y/b)^2}$$

Presentation of Results

Theoretical and experimental results obtained during aerodynamic studies are usually presented in the form of graphs of the functions C_L, C_D and C_m plotted against the angle of incidence a.

The curve for C_L against a is usually linear up to a

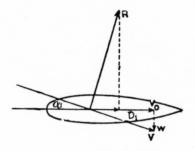

Fig. 16

maximum value of C_L and then curves away suddenly. This means that as the incidence of the wing is increased, the lift coefficient increases in direct proportion, until it reaches a certain static value, and then for further increases in incidence, the lift coefficient begins to fall. The incidence at which the maximum lift coefficient is obtained is known as the *stalling incidence*, and if in flight this incidence is exceeded, the wing is said to stall.

Eiffel, who made such an important contribution to the interpretation of experimental aerodynamics, plotted values of C_L against C_D to give what he called the wing polar. Figure 17 shows the characteristic curve for such a polar for the aerofoil section known as NACA 23012. The ratio of C_L to C_D is of fundamental importance in the calculation of wing characteristics, and consequently of aircraft performance.

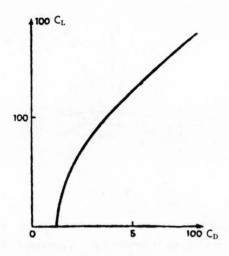

F<small>IG</small>. 17

Another type of polar is that used by Lilienthal, which instead of considering C_L and C_D directly, is based instead on the projections of the aerodynamic coefficients on the wing aerofoil profile and its normal. We can see from Figure 18 that the components of C_L and C_D are as follows:

$$C_n = C_L \cos a + C_D \sin a$$
$$C_t = C_D \cos a - C_L \sin a$$

Lilienthal's polar consisted of taking C_t as abscissa and C_n as ordinate. This enabled the relationship with the aerodynamic effect and the aerofoil chord to be readily followed, since this effect is graphically presented by the radius vector of the polar.

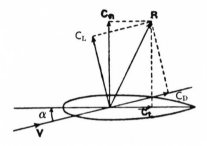

F$_{IG}$. 18

The pitching moment coefficient C_m can be written $C_m = C_{m0} - kC_L$, as is verified by experiment. The coefficient C_{m0} is generally negative.

The pitching moment leads us to a definition of the *center of pressure*. The center of pressure is the point through which the resultant aerodynamic force acts on the wing chord. It is the point about which the sum of the aerodynamic forces is zero. If d is used to denote the distance from the center of gravity to the wing leading edge, then it can be stated that $C_{mp} = C_{mG} + (d/c)C_L$, where c is the chord length. And taking into account the previous equation, we have:

$$C_{m0} - kC_L + (d/c)C_L = 0$$
$$- (C_{m0}/C_L) + k = d/c$$

Given a point F on the wing chord, distance x from the leading edge, then the pitching moment coefficient with regard to this point is $C_{mF} = C_{m0} - kC_L + (x/c)C_L$.

Thus if $x/c = k$, the pitching moment coefficient remains constant and equal to C_{m0} whatever the incidence.

It can be shown that in this case the induced drag coefficient is expressed in the form $C_{Di} = C_L^2/\pi\lambda$

The theoretical polar is thus the parabola $\pi\lambda C_D - C_L^2 = 0$, which is also called the *induced polar*. The induced drag is inversely proportional to the aspect ratio; a fact that affects the design of low-speed aircraft. The manifestation of a very high aspect ratio (with its associated low induced drag) is a high wing-span-to-wing-chord ratio, and many aircraft have been designed with very large wingspans to take special advantage of this aerodynamic phenomenon. In particular, the various man-powered aircraft projects being pursued in Great Britain utilize very high aspect ratios, so that the induced drag effects can be minimized.

The total drag on an aerofoil is in fact the sum of the induced drag and the profile drag $(C_{Di} + C_{Dp})$, and the profile drag is in turn composed of the form drag and the skin-friction drag.

The true polar is then written: $C_D = C_{Dp} + C_L^2/\pi\lambda$

Experiments show that wings of trapezoidal planform (which are especially common among subsonic aircraft) behave similarly to those of the ideal elliptical circulation distribution; and therefore, within limits, the above formulae apply to them.

Practical Calculation of Wing Lift

Let us consider a wing element parallel to the chord of thickness dy as shown in Figure 19.

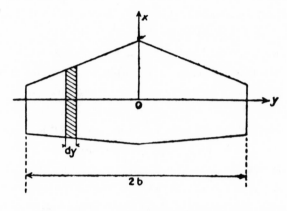

Fig. 19

The elementary lift on this small part of the wing can be written:

$$dL = \tfrac{1}{2}\rho V^2 \, dS \, c_L$$

where c_L is the local lift coefficient of the element. For any wing there is a relationship $c_L = f(y)$ that provides a value for the lift on any particular wing element as a function of its position along the span. This is called the *spanwise lift distribution* (Figure 20).

The total wing lift is then obtained by totaling the elementary lift forces on all the elements along the wing dL, thus:

$$L = \tfrac{1}{2}\rho C_L S V^2 = \int \tfrac{1}{2}\rho c_L V^2 \, dS \qquad \text{where } dS = c \, dy$$

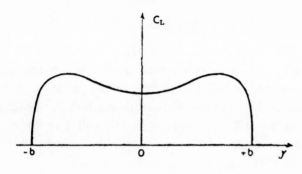

FIG. 20

We obtain the result:

$$C_L = \int_{-b}^{+b} (c.c_L/S) \, dy$$

To eliminate scale effect in the calculation, it is convenient to take as a unit length half the wing span b, so that $u = y/b$, and:

$$C_L = \frac{1}{S} \int_{-1}^{+1} c(u).c_L.b.du$$

or

$$C_L = \frac{\lambda}{2} \int_{-1}^{+1} p(u) \, du, \qquad \text{where } p(u) = 100 \, c_L(c/b)$$

$p(u)$ being called the local wing loading. In order to obtain the total lift C_L, the surface area of the space under the curve for local loading and above the u-axis is measured, and multiplied by half the aspect ratio.

Maximum Lift

We have noted, during study of the wing polar, that the lift passes through a maximum value at a certain angle of incidence, called the stalling incidence. Many experiments in the wind tunnel have shown that the maximum lift coefficient $C_{Lmax.}$ increases slightly with increase of the Reynolds number. However, the parameters most likely to influence wing lift are geometric parameters.

Tests carried out by Eiffel in a wind tunnel showed that cambered wings produce more lift than flat ones, under conditions of equal drag. The gradient of the lift curve dc_L/da was not changed, but the stalling incidence was increased.

Later studies showed that the condition of the wing surface has a considerable influence. This includes manufacturing irregularities in the aircraft skin, the roughness of paint finishes, and so on.

As already mentioned, these irregularities promote the transition of the boundary layer from laminar to turbulent flow, and the maximum lift coefficient is adversely affected.

The importance of wing-surface irregularities increases with the Reynolds number and is of major importance in the high-speed aircraft of today.

Manufacturing processes must be carefully controlled during the series production of an aircraft, for whereas a prototype may be virtually "hand-made," the need to keep production costs to a minimum and to turn out finished aircraft at the highest possible rate introduces the possibility of small variations in surface finish, which may critically affect the performance of the aircraft. The techniques for mass production to high standards have advanced very rapidly during the years since World War II: riveting of surface skins to the aircraft structure is now accomplished by the use of sunken rivets, the heads of which lie flush with the aircraft skin; metal-to-metal bonding avoids the use of rivets or bolts; and electric resistance welding enables a manufacturer to insure that the surface finish will not be impaired aerodynamically.

Some comparative figures will show the results usually obtained with typical aerofoil sections. One special profile used to obtain optimum performance is known as the *laminar profile aerofoil,* or more simply, the *laminar wing.* This has a maximum lift coefficient of about 1.2 and a stalling incidence of about 13 degrees. For low-speed aerofoils, high lift values can be obtained by using a high degree of camber, although the drag characteristics are poor. Typical figures are $C_L = 1.6$, and stalling incidence = 16 degrees.

Unfortunately, aircraft design has become a matter for increasing compromise. A wing profile that will allow the aircraft to cruise efficiently at high speed at high altitude will prove to be inadequate when it comes to landing, which explains why aircraft landing speeds have continued to rise, and why runways have had to be lengthened at regular intervals. Flight times over certain routes have been progressively reduced by the use of sophisticated design techniques involving the use of wing aerofoils efficient at high cruising speeds (and high-power engines with a low power-to-weight ratio), but the designer must use various devices to alter the characteristics of this wing profile, so that it is capable of producing the required lift at speeds close to the stall, and even perhaps of reducing the stalling speed. These aids to maximum lift fall under two headings: (1) those that involve a change in the wing profile; and (2) those that involve boundary-layer control.

The final choice of a maximum lift aid will be influenced by many factors: besides the attainment of maximum lift coefficient, these include accompanying drag increase, mechanical complexity and weight of the system and its controls. These are almost as important as the lift increment attained.

Maximum Lift by Change of Wing Profile

This consists for the most part in increasing the camber of the profile by either adding flaps or slots to the leading edge, or by adding flaps at the trailing edge.

The most commonly used leading-edge device is the Handley-Page slot. This consists of a small auxiliary slat, of approximately aerofoil shape, that in the neutral position forms the leading edge of the wing. At low speeds the slat moves forward (as shown in Figure 21) so that there is a small gap or slot at the front of the wing section through which air passes. This air has an advantageous effect on the flow over the upper surface of the wing at high incidences, and besides improving the lift distribution, it also delays the

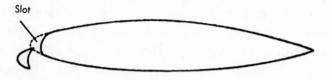

Slot

FIG. 21

stall. Figure 22 shows the Kruger flap or slat. This forms part of the lower surface in the neutral position, and hinges down to provide an extension of the leading edge. It is used only on high-speed aircraft, particularly airliners, to allow slow approaches at high incidences without the risk of stalling. The Kruger flap may hinge through as much as 100 degrees.

Another form of modification to the wing leading edge, which improves the low-speed characteristics, is the use of

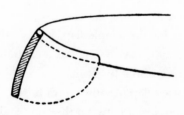

FIG. 22

variable leading edges, which may be inflatable, to increase the effective camber of the wing.

The high-lift leading-edge aids are in a particularly vulnerable part of the wing, as far as manufacturing difficulties are concerned, and they are usually used in conjunction with trailing-edge aids. These take the form of flaps:

a) The simple or plain flap. This forms part of the rear of the aerofoil profile and hinges down about an axis parallel to the wing span to effectively increase wing camber, as shown in Figure 23. Its principal use is for increasing the

Fig. 23

drag force at low speeds, although it does contribute to a higher lift coefficient.

b) The split flap. Only the lower surface of the aerofoil hinges down, as for the simple flap, leaving the upper surface intact. This type may be used as a continual flap across the ventral surface of the fuselage.

c) The slotted flap. Another form of the simple flap or plain flap, it opens a slot between the wing and the flap that is convergent, and as the flap rotates downward and the slot or gap opens, air passes from the lower surface to the upper surface to improve the pressure distribution over the wing at low speeds.

d) The Fowler flap. This consists of an aerofoil-shaped flap that again forms part of the wing trailing edge when not in use. As it moves downward, it also moves backward to provide a substantially increased wing area, as shown in Figure 24.

Fig. 24

The Fowler flap on a 12 to 15 per cent thick aerofoil section can give a lift increment of up to 80 per cent. Trailing-edge devices are easier to design and operate, because they can be made so that they do not materially affect the drag level at cruising speeds, and are not affected by such considerations as deicing, which poses a problem for leading-edge devices.

The following table compares the effectiveness of the different lift aids:

Configuration	$C_{Lmax.}$	Stalling Incidence
Wing alone	1.5	15°
Wing plus leading-edge aid	2.7	15°
Wing plus plain flaps	2.3	15°
Wing plus Fowler flaps	3.0	13°

Maximum Lift by Control of the Boundary Layer

Because, as we have seen above, lift is associated with the circulation around the wing, it is logical to attempt to improve the distribution of circulation in the boundary layer by re-energizing the air within the layer. Prandtl is believed to have been the first to propose some form of boundary-layer control, in 1904. Unfortunately, it was many years before his proposals were brought to fruition, and it was shortly before World War II when Arado in Germany drew attention to a system combining suction and blowing. Air sucked in over the flaps was blown out over the ailerons.

The power source for controlling the boundary layer can be air bled from the normal engines that propel the aircraft, or alternatively, the air can be supplied by an auxiliary power system. Although there are advantages in having an air supply that is not dependent on the aircraft prime mover, the compressor section of the turbojet engine provides a readily available source of such air without recourse to an entirely separate system and its additional complexity.

SUCTION

The effect of a suction slot is to prevent separation of the boundary layer by keeping the layer close to the aerofoil surface; furthermore, air molecules close to the wing that were in a state of stagnation are withdrawn. The increase of $C_{Lmax.}$ is higher for slots positioned well to the rear of the aerofoil, but the ideal place for the slot is at the point where separation normally originates.

In many practical applications, the suction slot is situated at the wing-flap junction.

BLOWING

The principal effect is to prevent separation of the boundary layer by the process of re-energizing. The velocity of the blown stream of air must be higher than the local air velocity alongside the slot.

As for suction, blowing is usually carried out from a slot just in front of the flaps. The increment in the lift coefficient obtained becomes greater as the slot becomes narrower. A simple study can be carried out:

Let us make dP the pressure change in the system, Q the rate of discharge of the air, and p the power necessary to pump the air. The total output of the system is the product of the thermodynamic power output η_{th} and the aerodynamic power output η_a. We can write:

$$\eta_{th} = dP.Q/p$$

The aerodynamic output depends on the configuration of the slots, their width and their position. It can be defined as the ratio of the lift increment dC_L due to the system, and the power used: $\eta_a = dC_L/dP.Q$.

Consequently total output η is given by:

$$\eta = \eta_{th} \times \eta_a = \frac{dP.Q}{p} \times \frac{dC_L}{dP.Q} = dC_L/p$$

This parameter (dC_L/p) is of fundamental importance in the comparison of boundary-layer control systems. Two other parameters must also be considered: the ratio p/W of the power necessary to operate the boundary-layer control to the total power output of the aircraft; and the ratio $\Delta\pi/p$ of the increase in weight due to the boundary-layer control system to power required for that system.

The first aircraft to enter service with blown flaps (or Attinello flaps, as they are sometimes called) was the Lockheed T2V Sea Star. Both the Supermarine Scimitar and the Lockheed F-104 Starfighter use blown flaps. The results of some tests carried out on an F-86 Sabrejet fighter are of interest. The leading edge was replaced by a porous stainless-steel plate, and boundary-layer blowing was accomplished through this porous plate. A C_L of 1.8 at an incidence of 24 degrees was obtained, compared with the previous highest value 1.1 at 12 degrees.

The reduction of take-off and landing speeds for carrier-based aircraft is essential, and the British Navy's Blackburn Buccaneer strike fighter makes extensive use of boundary-layer blowing techniques.

The Jet Flap

A similar manifestation of aerodynamic control by the use of an auxiliary air supply is the jet flap. This high-lift technique has been the subject of much experimental and theoretical work, especially in Great Britain, and a special research aircraft has been constructed by the Hunting company under a British government contract to carry out full-scale testing of jet-flap practicability. The mechanical flap is replaced by a sheet of air extending downward and backward from the wing trailing edge; this sheet is produced by ejecting engine air from a small flap or lip carrying the ejector nozzle. It is, of course, possible to use the full exhaust from the engine, so that the gas sheet is directed rearward for propulsion in normal flight and then deflected downward to give high lift coefficients during the landing maneuver, or for take-off.

Figure 25 shows the jet flap inclined downward for

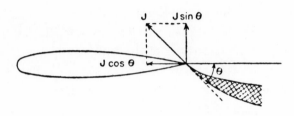

Fɪɢ. 25

high-lift generation. Considering the system in two dimensions, we can see that the first apparent result will be that the jet will mix with the surrounding air, thus absorbing the boundary layer at the rear of the aerofoil. Air moving over the wing upper surface is attracted downward by the jet flap—being accelerated in the process—and a lower-upper surface pressure distribution results, which gives rise to a higher lift force. This additional lift force (whose line of action is approximately at the mid-chord point) can be added to the vertical component of the jet thrust. Results obtained have shown that the total lift due to the system is equal to several times the jet thrust alone. This is in fact a purely aerodynamic increase, which is dependent on the jet coefficient C_j, defined by:

$$C_j = J / \tfrac{1}{2}\rho V_0{}^2{}_c$$

where J is the jet thrust force, and c is the aerofoil chord.

When C_j varies from 0.25 to 4.5, the ratio of lift increase goes from 6.8 to 2.3. Early experimental studies showed that the jet could be deflected through 90 degrees without the flow over the upper surface of the wing separating, and it is thus possible to obtain extremely high values of C_L with a low wing incidence.

Blowing smoke from the jet flap slot enables us to observe the characteristics of the flow distribution in relation to those predicted by theory. A suction bubble forms on the upper surface of the wing, and becomes larger as the value of C_j is increased. Mixing of the jet with the surrounding air creates an additional drag force, which we can represent by means of the jet drag coefficient C_{Dj}. In fact this coefficient depends upon the exit velocity of the jet flap stream, and more exactly on the product ρV.

If we denote quantities associated with the jet by j, and quantities associated with the free stream by 0:
for $\rho_j V_j$ greater than $\rho_0 V_0$, there is a drag force (C_{Dj} greater than 0); for $\rho_j V_j$ less than $\rho_0 V_0$, there is a thrust force (C_{Dj} less than 0).

These results were proved using a jet of hydrogen with a range of values of exit velocity.

The center of thrust is situated to the rear of the midchord point and moves back as C_j increases. It is independent of the angle of outlet of the jet.

Tests indicate that the efficiency of the jet flap diminishes rapidly as the aspect ratio is reduced, although efficiency increases with the Mach number and is not affected by the presence of shock waves.

Although it appears to be so efficient, there are a number of engineering problems to be overcome with the jet flap, for the lift of the aircraft becomes almost entirely dependent on the operation of the engines that provide the jet flap. A combination of the conventional flap and the jet flap appears to provide the best compromise, with the jet stream emerging from a slot situated above and in front of the mechanical flap, as shown in Figure 26. Moving the

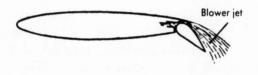

FIG. 26

mechanical flap affords simple control of the jet flap stream, during flight.

The chord length of the mechanical flap part of the jet flap is usually contained within the rear 3 to 15 per cent of the wing chord (more often the lower value). The total lift derived from the combination of the mechanical flap with jet flap is not the same as the sum of the lift derived from the mechanical flap alone and the jet flap alone. Extensive work on the jet flap principle has been carried out at the National Gas Turbine Establishment in Great Britain, and results from this work show, for example, that if a jet flap alone gives a C_L of 5.4 and the mechanical flap gives a C_L of 1.8, then a combination of the two types of flap will give a C_L of 6.1.

Drag

The drag coefficient of a wing can be written $C_D = C_{Dp} + C_{Di}$, where C_{Dp} is the profile drag coefficient, and C_{Di} is the induced drag coefficient.

The profile drag can itself be split into the skin-friction drag—which is independent of the wing incidence—and the form drag, which varies considerably at the higher values of the lift coefficient.

The profile drag can be evaluated in the wind tunnel by a method (devised by Betz) that consists of measuring the pressure distribution across the wake behind the aerofoil, and integrating these values across the wake.

The profile drag, as its name implies, depends largely on the aerofoil profile or shape, and it is possible to design such a profile to give minimum drag by keeping the boundary layer laminar over all or the greater part of the surface. These sections are therefore known as *laminar sections* or *aerofoils*.

The design of these laminar profiles results in a maximum thickness point as far back as perhaps mid-chord. One of the disadvantages of these wings is that although the profile drag is very low at the low wing incidences associated with cruising flight, at higher values of incidence (for example, when the aircraft is maneuvering, taking off or landing) the drag becomes quite high. Furthermore, the laminar wing is extremely sensitive to small surface irregularities, and for this reason close control must be exercised over the manufacture of a wing having a laminar profile for maximum effectiveness.

The boundary-layer systems that we have just discussed with respect to increases of lift may also be adapted to provide increases or decreases in the drag. One of the main applications of boundary-layer suction is to produce a laminar boundary layer, with its attendant low drag values, and the Handley-Page research team led by Dr. Lachmann in Great Britain, and the team led by Dr. Pffenniger in the United States, are carrying out work aimed at applying this principle to a whole range of aircraft designs.

4 / The Wing At High Speeds

As we saw in Chapter 1, when the velocity of the air flow around an aircraft or wing reaches a value corresponding to about Mach 0.7, the effects of compressibility begin to be felt.

This type of flow has different characteristics from the flow at lower speeds—which can be regarded as incompressible—and it is therefore to be expected that at high subsonic speeds the low-speed theory of the wing no longer applies. Compressibility has been studied for many years, and much theoretical and experimental work has been carried out to establish a valid wing theory for this speed range.

This theory shows that the values of the lift and drag coefficients are related to the coefficients of incompressible flow in the following manner:

$$C_L = \frac{C_{Li}}{\sqrt{1 - M_0^2}}$$

$$C_D = \frac{C_{Di}}{\sqrt{1 - M_0{}^2}}$$

where the symbol i corresponds to the values in incompressible flow. These relationships were discovered independently by Prandtl and Glauert about 1930, and they are therefore known as the *Prandtl-Glauert relationships*. In the same way:

$$\frac{dC_L}{da} = \frac{1}{\sqrt{1 - M^2}} \left(\frac{dC_L}{da} \right)_i$$

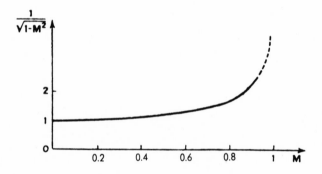

FIG. 27

Figure 27 shows how the value of $1/\sqrt{1 - M^2}$ varies with increase of Mach number up to one. The term $1/\sqrt{1 - M^2}$ is known as the *Glauert factor*.

Basically this relationship is only valid for wings of infinite aspect ratio; for finite wings the relationship is more complicated. Furthermore the relationships cease to be valid as the value of M approaches one.

The thickness/chord ratio of the aerofoil profile must be taken into account when using these relationships, as they only hold true for values between 6 and 16 per cent. Above 16 per cent thickness/chord ratio, the lift predicted by the relationship is higher than that actually obtained.

Since the velocity of the free-stream air increases as it flows around the aerofoil in flight, it is apparent that although the aircraft itself may be flying at a speed lower than Mach 1, somewhere on the wing surface the local velocity will be that of the speed of sound. Once the Mach number of unity has been reached at some point on the wing, the aircraft is said to be flying at the critical Mach number, $M_{crit.}$ and the Prandtl-Glauert relationships are no longer valid.

If the speed of the aircraft increases still further, shock waves form on the aerofoil. We have already seen that across shock waves there are abrupt changes in the pressure, temperature, velocity and density of the air. Within the boundary layer the shock wave does not exist, for the air velocity there is lower than the external flow velocity, and subsonic. As the air pressure behind the shock wave is higher than that in front, this exerts an effect on the boundary layer, producing a secondary shock wave, which combined with the primary shock wave produces a shock system shaped like the Greek letter lambda, and is therefore called a *lambda shock wave*. This name was given to the effect by the famous Swiss aerodynamicist Ackerett, who is responsible for much of the theory of supersonic flow.

Behind the lambda shock wave the boundary layer continues to thicken, then separates, producing a thick wake that gives rise to a large drag increment. This is due to the increase in form drag, which is at this stage about seven times greater than the skin-friction drag. This large increase in form drag becomes a formidable obstacle to the aircraft as it attempts to accelerate from subsonic to supersonic speeds; and as a result of this feature, and the control and stability problems associated with flight in the region of Mach 1, these compressibility manifestations are known as the *sound barrier*. As we shall see later, this "barrier" can be surmounted without too much difficulty, by sophisticated design techniques and the use of high-thrust engines. The boundary-layer separation that results from the presence of the shock wave also causes a sudden loss in lift—a reduction especially marked in wing profiles with a high thickness/chord ratio.

Figure 28 shows how the lift and drag coefficients vary

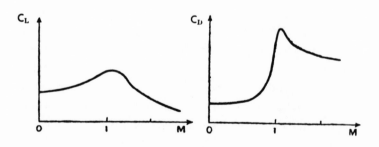

Fig. 28

with increasing Mach number. It can be seen that C_L continues to increase until just above the speed of sound, where it falls abruptly and then gradually; C_D rises abruptly at about Mach 1 and then falls off again. At the same time, the position of the center of lift changes, moving from approximately the quarter-chord point to a position near the mid-chord point; it then comes forward again at speeds in excess of Mach 1 (Figure 29). As a result, there is a varia-

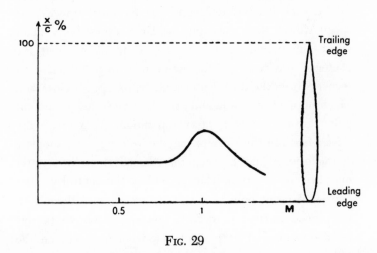

Fɪɢ. 29

tion in the pitching-moment coefficient, and the aircraft is difficult to control longitudinally, at transonic speeds. Once again we find that thick aerofoils have the poorer characteristics at transonic speeds, because the center of lift of these profiles moves much farther than for a thin aerofoil.

Control Surfaces at Transonic Speeds

Longitudinal control is generally attained (except in tailless aircraft) by the deflection up or down of elevators mounted on the aircraft's tail unit.

At transonic speeds the reduction of wing lift is accompanied by a modification of the flow over the tail unit behind the wing, and the net result is a nose-down movement that sends the aircraft into a steep dive. The normal corrective action is to pull back on the pilot's control column in the cockpit, thus deflecting the elevators upward; at speeds lower than those for which compressibility takes effect, this action causes the aircraft to pitch about the center of gravity so that the nose comes up and the aircraft recovers from the dive. Unfortunately, for speeds close to a Mach number of 1, a lambda shock wave forms on the tail unit, causing boundary-layer separation. As a result the effectiveness of the elevator may be lost, or worse, the flow characteristics may be such that the effect of the control may become reversed. That is, pulling the control column back will result only in a still steeper dive. Although all high-speed aircraft now have power controls or power-assisted controls that prevent aerodynamic forces on the tail from being transmitted back to the pilot, tail effectiveness at transonic speeds is achieved principally by using a variable-incidence unit, which can be operated through a range of incidences relative to the wing chord.

Supersonic Flow

Ackerett established a theory for supersonic flow as early as 1925. It led to the conclusion that the lift is proportional to the incidence, according to the following relationship:

$$C_L = \frac{4a}{\sqrt{M^2 - 1}}$$

In other words, all wing profiles have the same lift, regardless of their shape, and the lift coefficient decreases as the Mach number increases.

As far as the drag is concerned, d'Alembert's paradox no longer holds good at supersonic speeds, and there exists a drag—*compressibility drag*—that is the component of the resultant force in the direction of the free-stream velocity.

The best wing profiles for supersonic flight are very thin symmetrical shapes, such as double-wedge, rhomboidal or bi-convex profiles.

The Influence of Planform on Wing Characteristics

The first method for delaying the drag rise on an aerofoil or wing at high subsonic speeds was evolved by Lippisch, and involves sweeping the leading edge of the wing backward.

As Figure 30 shows, air of velocity V flowing toward a swept wing has two effective components: the first, V_N, is perpendicular to the wing leading edge, and the second, V_T, is parallel to the leading edge. The component V_T does not affect the pressure distribution around the wing, but may affect the boundary layer. The swept wing in fact behaves at a velocity V like a straight wing placed in a flow having a velocity of V_N, and if the angle of wing sweepback is ϕ, then $V_N = V \cos \phi$. The critical Mach number for a

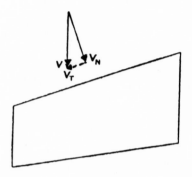

Fɪɢ. 30

wing swept at an angle ϕ is then obtained by multiplying the critical Mach number of the equivalent straight wing by $1/\cos \phi$. Actual results show that this relationship is an over-simplification, and the factor $1/\sqrt{\cos \phi}$ gives a closer approximation to the benefit actually derived from wing sweep. There is a considerable drag reduction, as Figure 31 shows, with the swept wing compared with the straight wing at Mach numbers around and above a value of one, although the swept wing has a higher drag at low speeds. The center of lift of the swept wing undergoes a comparatively minor displacement in contrast to the movement of the center of lift of the unswept wing at transonic speeds.

One of the disadvantages of the highly swept wing is the relatively low lift coefficient it produces. Certain versions of the F-86 Sabrejet swept-wing fighter are fitted with

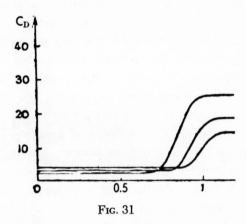

FIG. 31

1. Straight wing;　2. Swept wing;　3. Delta wing

leading-edge slats that extend automatically under their own weight at low speeds to facilitate control of the air flow over the swept wing, and to give the aircraft a lower stalling speed and improved maneuverability at low speeds. The use of plain flaps with swept-wing aircraft is primarily to give a high drag coefficient on the landing run, so that the aircraft's speed falls off quickly, although at small flap-down angles there is also a contribution to the lift coefficient.

The poor characteristics of the swept wing at low speeds has led to higher landing speeds, for two reasons: the stalling speed has gone up; and the wing loading is so high that the margin for error while maneuvering at low speeds prior to landing is great. The swept-wing aircraft is therefore landed at a speed well above the stall, preferably in a straight approach in which height and airspeed are progressively lost. A swept-wing aircraft is always flown onto the ground in a positive manner, as compared with the technique of holding off and then stalling just as the wheels touch the ground that is used with most conventional straight-wing aircraft. Because the swept-wing aircraft is designed for minimum drag at high speed, it is aerodynamically clean, with the result that a long run is needed to decelerate to a halt: besides the use of flaps to provide high drag on the landing run, these aircraft must make use of such other devices as wheel-disc brakes and tail parachutes to provide further deceleration. Such high-speed aircraft, especially fighters, invariably have air brakes, which are primarily for use at high speeds but which are also used for providing extra drag on the landing run. The high wing-loading also means that the aircraft must accelerate to a speed well above the stall before it leaves the ground, which again means that long runways are needed.

A novel idea for giving the aircraft the advantage of a swept wing at high speeds for economic cruise at altitude, combined with the advantages of a straight wing at low speeds, has been suggested by Dr. Barnes Wallis, a British engineer. This involves the use of variable geometry, in that the wings can be pivoted about hinges at the wing roots so that the wing is straight at take-off and landing, and is then moved to a maximum sweep-back position for cruise at supersonic speeds. A number of designs using this variable geometry are being studied, principally for military fighter aircraft, although the idea has great pertinence in the economic design of supersonic airliners. But although the system has such obvious advantages, there are a number of major design problems: the design of the hinge is particularly complicated, and the aircraft must be capable of landing at a reasonable speed in the event the hinge malfunctions and the aircraft is forced to land with the wings in the highly swept position.

The advent of the Bristol Siddeley BS-53 Pegasus engine, with its four swiveling nozzles each supplying thrust that can be vectored downward to give vertical jet thrust lift for vertical take-off, or backward to give thrust for normal horizontal flight, is likely to revolutionize the design of future high-speed aircraft; Britain's Hawker P-1127 strike fighter is the first of this new generation of aircraft. Alongside this particular use of jet thrust for lift purposes is the development by Rolls-Royce of special light-weight engines for the same application. These small engines are mounted vertically in the fuselage to give thrust at take-off and landing, and are not used throughout the normal cruising flight (power for this phase of flight being provided by a normal horizontally mounted engine). These small jet-lift engines are already being developed to give a thrust in pounds that is sixteen times the weight of the engine itself. Thus it is likely that the trend toward longer runways has reached its peak, and that the years ahead will witness the development of aircraft that can operate from extremely short runways or from helicopter-type platforms.

Finally, on the subject of the use of engines to assist during take-off and landing with purposes other than propulsion, we may note that reverse-pitch propellers and reverse-thrust jet engines are used extensively to aid deceleration during the landing ground run, and that the two outer engines of the three-engined de Havilland Trident airliner are used to provide reverse thrust in flight for rapid deceleration from the cruising speed.

The Crescent Wing and the Delta Wing

The crescent-shaped wing used on the Handley-Page Victor bomber is another solution to the problem of delaying the compressibility effects. The crescent- or scimitar-shaped wing has compound sweepback. As the engines are buried in the wing roots, the wing has maximum thickness at this position, and the angle of sweepback is therefore maximum. Further away from the wing root, the angle of sweep is reduced and the wing is thinner, so that at the wing tip the angle of sweepback is at a minimum and tip stalling is avoided. This progressive change in the sweepback angle and wing thickness also allows the size of the wing structural components to be progressively reduced (see Figure 32). The efficiency of the ailerons is thereby improved at low speeds, and the aeroelasticity effects due to the change of the lift distribution at high subsonic speeds are minimized.

The delta wing, which was originally suggested by the German aerodynamicist Lippisch, uses two factors to reduce drag at high speeds. We have already seen that sweeping back the leading edge delays the effects of compressibility. Another way of doing this is to reduce the thickness/chord ratio. In the delta- or triangular-shaped wing the value of

FIG. 32

the chord length is very high, and consequently the desired low thickness/chord ratios can be achieved. The low aspect ratio also contributes to low drag at high speeds, and the delta-wing planform has therefore been adopted for many transonic and supersonic aircraft: the Avro-Vulcan bomber, the Gloster Javelin fighter, the Convair Hustler bomber and many others. (For example, the French Dassault Mirage III-D supersonic fighter has an aspect ratio of 1.98, a thickness/chord ratio of 3.5 per cent, and a leading-edge sweepback of 60 degrees.)

Figure 31 compares the drag characteristics of the three types of wing—straight, swept and delta—as a function of the Mach number. The delta wing has a C_D almost half that of the straight wing. Although the lift characteristics of the delta wing cannot be compared to those of a low-speed straight wing, its properties are comparatively good for a high-speed configuration. It is interesting to compare the wing loadings and landing speeds of two modern fighters capable of a speed of Mach 2.2. The first is a delta-wing aircraft, the Mirage III, already mentioned; it has a wing loading of 48 lb./sq. ft. and a landing speed of 150 m.p.h. The Lockheed F-104 Starfighter has a very thin straight wing of 3.36 thickness/chord ratio, an aspect ratio of 2.97, a wing loading of about 90 lb./sq. ft., and a landing speed of 164 m.p.h. Lest it be thought that the two types of wing compare favorably at low speeds, we should note that whereas the Mirage III has no flaps, the F-104 uses flaps with a boundary-layer control system that blows compressed air from the engine over the flaps at any flap setting higher than 15 degrees, to give the aircraft a lower landing speed. One disadvantage of the delta planform is that approaches must be made at high angles of incidence when landing, which denies the pilot the best view of the runway. Nevertheless the delta wing reigns supreme for high-speed aircraft, because its configuration allows the landing gear and fuel to be stowed in the wing, and structural design is simplified. The comparatively low wing loading gives the delta aircraft a high degree of maneuverability at altitude, and the complexities of flaps and tailplane can in general be dispensed with; control is exercised by means of surfaces at the trailing edge that do the work of both ailerons and elevators and are therefore known as *elevons*. Once the aircraft has passed through the transonic region (Mach 0.85 to Mach 1.25), the thin, straight wing once more becomes aerodynamically acceptable. However, even truly supersonic fighters (like the Starfighter and the Mirage III) do not spend the whole of their operational lives at Mach 2.2, and it is therefore important that they have low drag in the transonic region. In fact, swept, delta and straight wings all provide solutions to the high wave drag associated with transonic and supersonic flight, and depending on the design technique, all wing planforms can give comparable high-speed performance. Again we quote the examples of the delta Mirage III and the straight-wing Starfighter, and to them we add the swept-wing English Electric Lightning fighter. All are capable of Mach 2.2, but their wing loadings are very different. The delta aircraft has the best landing characteristics in terms of speed and maneuverability close to the stall.

Aerodynamic Heating at High Speeds

The temperature of the air in the boundary layer increases from a value T_0, the temperature of the free-stream flow, to a value T_i—called the *stagnation temperature*—at the surface of the wing. We can express this temperature rise in the following way:

$$T_i - T_0 = \tfrac{1}{2} \frac{V^2}{c_p}$$

where V is the free-stream velocity and c_p is the specific heat of the air at constant pressure.

We can write instead:

$$\left(T_i = T_0\, 1 + \frac{M^2}{5} \right)$$

This is a theoretical result, which only holds good for a body that is thermally isolated. In fact, other thermal effects —including conduction and radiation—also exert influences. The actual temperature at the body surface depends on

whether the boundary layer is laminar or turbulent: the
heat received at the surface is perhaps as much as ten times
greater in the turbulent case, due to the violent forced-
convection process that takes place in a turbulent boundary
layer. As speed increases, the heat radiated from the surface
increases, according to Stefan's law, which says that heat
emitted is proportional to the fourth power of the absolute
temperature.

The net result is that the actual temperature increase is
15 per cent lower than that given by the formula. Figure 33

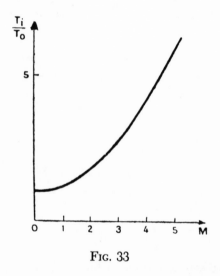

FIG. 33

shows the temperature/Mach number relationship in
graphic form.

The heating problem at high Mach numbers has often

been referred to as the *heat barrier*, for at one time the problems associated with travel at these speeds seemed insoluble. However, the use of materials such as stainless steel and titanium that have excellent strength properties at high temperatures, and the clever design of cooling systems and heat shields, are likely to overcome most of the heating problems. We should remember that even a long-range supersonic airliner traveling at Mach 3 starts at a low body temperature, and that its surfaces are only submitted to maximum heating effects for perhaps an hour and a half at most. It is unlikely that in this time the whole aircraft will reach the maximum temperature of the stagnation point, and the use of the fuel as a coolant can keep the temperature within acceptable limits. As the speed rises, so the journey time decreases and the use of ablation material that takes up its latent heat of vaporization delays the temperature rise of the aircraft structures. In the case of re-entry space vehicles, the vehicle is submitted to tremendous temperature only for a matter of minutes, and ablative shields appear to provide adequate protection.

Supersonic Bangs

When an aircraft exceeds the speed of sound in the course of a high-speed dive, observers on the ground in the aircraft's path hear one and perhaps two explosion-like noises (which may vary considerably in intensity) called *supersonic bangs*. This phenomenon was a regular feature of flying displays until recent years, when damage to buildings and inconvenience to the public in general brought the intentional production of such bangs to a halt over built-up areas.

This twin noise, or *double bang*, was at first attributed to the arrival of the shock waves, from, first the aircraft wing, and second, the aircraft tail unit. However, the distance between the two is so small in relation to the speed of sound that this cannot be accepted as a valid explanation of the double bang heard on the ground. An explanation generally accepted as more plausible is that when the aircraft exceeds the speed of sound the noises it produces (such as those from the engine) accumulate along with the large pressure change due to the shock waves to produce a very powerful wave, since they are traveling at the same speed as the aircraft; this sound wave will grow stronger the longer the aircraft stays at or above the speed of sound. As the aircraft exceeds the speed of sound, and then stays at a speed greater than Mach 1 for a short period of time, it decelerates again for the pullout from the dive, and then, as the speed drops, passes through Mach 1 again. In other words, the two bangs heard on the ground are, first, the aircraft's acceleration through Mach 1, and, secondly, its deceleration through Mach 1. We should note that because the Mach number is the relationship between the aircraft's speed and the speed of sound at any particular altitude, as the aircraft dives the speed of sound increases (because the air is denser) and the Mach number of the aircraft falls, without the aircraft's speed necessarily changing in any way.

When an aircraft exceeds the speed of sound in level

flight at any particular altitude, it trails behind it a shock wave of high intensity. This shock wave travels across the ground as the aircraft continues to maintain a supersonic speed, and the pressure rise produces at ground level a sound akin to a bang, along with blast characteristics. The intensity of these effects on the ground depends on a large number of factors, including the aircraft's Mach number, altitude and aerodynamic characteristics. Now that military aircraft are capable of speeds of Mach 2.2 in level flight, it has been necessary to restrict their peacetime training flying at this speed to flights over water, or uninhabited areas, so that the inconvenience caused the public by the trailing shock waves will be minimized. A similar problem arises with the operation of a supersonic airliner, for the shock wave from a Mach 3 transport carrying 150 people can produce a very large pressure rise at ground level. Much theoretical work has been done on this problem, and the Convair B-58 Hustler is at the time of writing being used in a test program to establish the actual pressure rise at ground level caused by an aircraft flying at various supersonic speeds at various heights.

Figure 34 shows the principal phases of a dive in which the aircraft briefly reaches a supersonic speed, with the associated wave fronts.

Hypersonic Flow

Flow is considered to be hypersonic when it is traveling relative to a body—aircraft, missile or wind-tunnel model—at more than five times the speed of sound. With

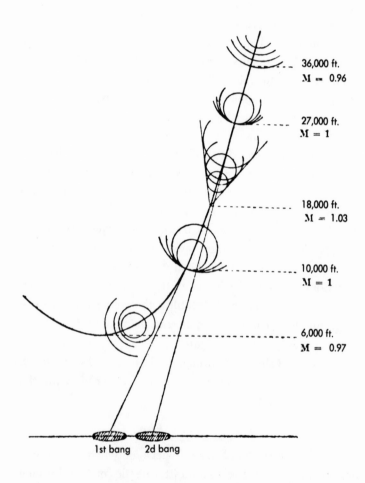

36,000 ft.
M = 0.96

27,000 ft.
M = 1

18,000 ft.
M = 1.03

10,000 ft.
M = 1

6,000 ft.
M = 0.97

1st bang   2d bang

Fig. 34

the large-scale advent of satellite launchings and recoveries, speeds of Mach 5 and more are almost an everyday occurrence. The North American X-15 is currently the fastest manned aircraft in the world, having achieved a speed in excess of Mach 6.0 at about 100,000 feet. The X-15 is a rocket-powered research aircraft (actually, a number have been constructed) carried aloft under the wing of another aircraft, and then released at altitude when its rocket motor is started. Thus it can accelerate to high speed and climb to high altitudes without having to carry the fuel required for normal take-off and climb.

Figure 35 shows the expected type of flow around a body at hypersonic speeds. The nose shock wave is blunt or rounded, rather than the straight shock experienced at supersonic speeds. The shock wave is not attached to the nose of the body, but is said to be detached, with a region

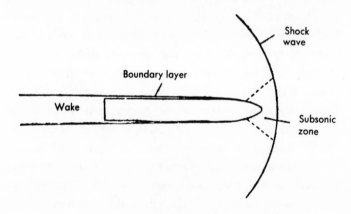

Fig. 35

of subsonic flow surrounding the nose. A boundary layer and a wake exist as in any other speed regime.

In the space immediately behind the shock wave, and adjacent to the blunt nose of the body, the air is at extremely high temperature. We have already seen that there is a rise in temperature across a shock wave; and for the one under consideration, we have hypersonic flow on one side of the shock, and subsonic flow on the other side. Thus there is a very rapid rise in temperature, and consequently the flow in the region breaks down into particles of atomic size; it is said to *dissociate*. The diatomic molecules of oxygen and nitrogen dissociate into atoms.

When a molecule crosses the shock wave, the translational energy is converted into a vibrational energy, which produces a thickening of the shock wave. This thickening effect increases away from the nose of the body: the thickness of the shock is inversely proportional to the density of the air, and increases with altitude. As a result of this partial dissociation of the air that occurs adjacent to the nose of a body in hypersonic flow, the electron distribution also changes, and ionization occurs. This ionization of the air makes it difficult if not impossible to transmit radio messages through this layer of air. A practical result of this phenomenon is that when space satellites re-enter the earth's atmosphere, a hypersonic bow wave forms around the craft, and quite apart from the intense heating to which the body is subjected, the layer of ionized air around the craft prevents radio signals describing the re-entering body's path from being received on earth.

This dissociation process also gives rise to various forms of association, which are of considerable importance from the viewpoint of heat of reaction; that is, heat gained or lost during the association process. For example, oxygen and nitrogen in the air re-form to give nitrous oxide, NO_2, which is an endothermic reaction.

Theoretical and experimental studies that have been carried out allow us to set down some fundamental results. For a cone-cylinder combination—a missile configuration particularly suitable for high speeds—the lift increases with the length of the cylindrical part. Thus it can be appreciated that the part played by the fuselage in providing lift is of some significance at hypersonic speeds. Finally, we should mention that the laminar boundary layer is more stable in hypersonic flow than in the supersonic regime.

Many of these effects have been studied in areodynamics laboratories. In the next chapter we shall discuss the facilities used in such study.

5 / *Aerodynamic Testing:*
Wind Tunnels

From the end of the nineteenth century, when physicists and engineers began to take more than a passing interest in the characteristics of flow around the simpler body shapes (such as spheres and flat plates), it became apparent that some form of reliable apparatus was required to reproduce the flow effects accurately. After attempts were made with a wide variety of systems—including whirling arms, free fall and powered trollies—the wind tunnel became universally accepted as the most suitable system. Today a vast number of wind tunnels are in use, capable of reproducing flow effects at speeds from a few feet per second to hypersonic speeds.

Classification

Wind tunnels can be classified either according to the flow velocity in a certain part of the tunnel, or according to the way the moving air stream is produced. The most common tunnels are those in which a fan or compressor is used to insure that the velocity of the air at the working section is as required. These tunnels may be open-section (in which air drawn in from the atmosphere passes around the test model at the required velocity and is then returned to the atmosphere), or closed section (in which the same air is continually circulated around a closed circuit). Small, high-speed tunnels may be of the intermittent type. Here the time of operation is limited, and the tunnel works on an expansion system in which either (1) compressed air from a reservoir is allowed to escape at high velocity through the working section; or (2) air is sucked in from the atmosphere by creating a vacuum downstream from the working section.

Open-Circuit Wind Tunnels

The first tunnel built by Eiffel, in 1912, was of the open-circuit variety. It had a convergent section at entry so that air was immediately sucked into a large chamber where the test model was mounted. A divergent section fitted with a fan formed the air outlet, as shown in Figure 36. The fan provided the source of energy for producing the required moving stream of air. Subject to flow losses due to friction, the maximum speed in such an open-section tunnel is reached at the narrowest section, and it is here that the model is mounted, at what we call the *working section*. As it crosses the chamber, the air flow is not restricted by material boundaries, and is therefore said to be *open-jet*.

The operation of such a wind tunnel leads inevitably

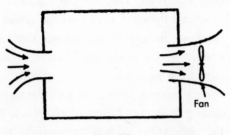

Fig. 36

to energy losses: in the collector and diffuser (due to friction); in the open-jet section; and so on. The sum of these losses determines the size and power output of the fan.

The air drawn in directly from the atmosphere is often turbulent, and would upset the flow around the model in the test section. Therefore a honeycomb grid or gauze screen is used to remove the turbulence.

One example of this type of wind tunnel is the Chalais-Meudon tunnel belonging to the French O.N.E.R.A. organization (Office National d'Études et de Recherches Aéronautiques). The jet is elliptical in shape (about 53 by 26 feet), and is produced by six fans that develop a total of 4,400 kw.

However, most modern tunnels are of the *return-flow* type. This category of tunnel (which was used by Prandtl at the Göttingen Institute in 1909) consists of a settling chamber, a contraction section and a diffuser section joined by ducting with four distinct bends. Between the contraction section and the diffuser section is the working section, in which model tests are performed. This section may be either open- or closed-jet. Thus the same air circulates continually throughout the circuit, and is kept in motion by the action of the fans. In high-speed tunnels the air becomes heated due to the nature of the wind-tunnel cycle, so that a cooling system must be used.

There are various solutions to this problem. For example, a cooling fluid may be circulated inside the tunnel walls. Or the circulating air may be partially replaced by cold air, so that conditions in the working section remain constant yet the temperature of the air in the tunnel is kept at an acceptable level. A typical closed-circuit tunnel, then, might have an electrically driven fan that moves the air to produce the required air speed in the working section, followed by a gradually diverging section of ducting that leads via cascades of corner vanes, honeycomb grids and gauze screens to the settling chamber, which is merely a uniform cross-section of ducting. The contraction section leads the air to the working section, while increasing its velocity to the required amount. Beyond the working section is the diffuser section. It has an angle not greater than about 6 degrees in which the kinetic energy of the air is converted to pressure energy. The air proceeds via further ducting and corner cascades to the driving fan.

Wind-tunnel methods are essentially comparative, and a wind tunnel can never give the information that full-scale flight tests can. To effectively compare wind-tunnel and full-scale free-flight tests, the Reynolds numbers of the two

regimes must be similar. A normal tunnel has a comparatively low Reynolds number capability, so that another
device is used to achieve the desirable higher Reynolds
number: the variable-density tunnel. In 1925 a variable-
density tunnel was constructed at Britain's National Physical Laboratory and models were tested at pressures up to
25 atmospheres.

Supersonic Wind Tunnels

Whatever their type, supersonic wind tunnels consist
essentially of a convergent-divergent nozzle (Fig. 37) that

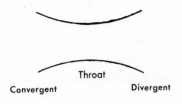

Throat

Convergent   Divergent

Fig. 37

operates as follows: Air arriving at the divergent section of
the nozzle has a subsonic speed of less than Mach 1, a speed
that increases as the air passes through the convergent section. The nozzle design is such that the air reaches the
speed of sound at the throat; and due to this feature, the
expansion of the flow beyond the throat produces an even
higher velocity in the divergent section, until the flow
reaches the speed required, in the working section.

The shape of the nozzle plays an important part in the Mach number achieved at the working section, and since any one throat shape can only produce one working-section Mach number, it is necessary to design supersonic tunnels so that the nozzle shape can be varied. This can be done in two ways: either the nozzle section can be removable, so that a number of differently shaped nozzles or liners can be inserted in the tunnel circuit to give the desired speed; or the tunnel walls can be flexible, so that the shape can be altered by means of some form of external mechanical system. At Britain's Royal Aircraft Establishment (at Bedford, England) there is a supersonic tunnel that can produce speeds between Mach 2.5 and Mach 5 in a working section measuring 4 by 3 feet; it has a nozzle section consisting of flexible steel plates operated by hydraulic jacks to give the required nozzle profile. This method of producing different Mach numbers in the working section of a single tunnel is obviously the most suitable, because it allows Mach numbers to be changed during a test run; whereas the interchangeable-liner type of supersonic tunnel permits use of only a limited number of predetermined Mach numbers, and then merely one at a time. The cost and complexity of the variable-contour tunnel make it unlikely that the interchangeable-liner type will be entirely superseded.

A return to the upstream flow conditions takes place after the air leaves the nozzle, by means of a system of shock waves. The pressure drop thus produced is isentropic (that is, without any exchange of thermal energy and in a reversible manner), and is limited by the liquefaction of the air. For Mach numbers higher than 5, it therefore becomes necessary to increase the temperature of the air upstream of the nozzle.

In return-flow tunnels, nozzles with double throats may be used in preference to the single-throat ones. This double-throated nozzle (Fig. 38) has the following characteristics:

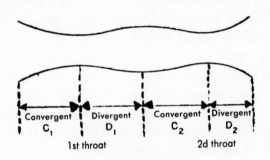

FIG. 38
Two-throat type wind tunnel

(1) A primary section C_1 that increases the speed of the air until it reaches the value of the local speed of sound in the first throat;

(2) A divergent section D_1 in which the flow speed continues to increase, reaching a maximum value at the end of this divergent section;

(3) The working section, followed by a second nozzle with a convergent section C_2 in which the flow speed decreases according to supersonic flow theory until the second throat; and

(4) A divergent section D_2 in which the speed increases again, before becoming subsonic again across a shock-wave system.

Supersonic flow is only achieved if the ratio p_c/p_0 between the first throat pressure and the upstream pressure in the tube reaches a value of 0.527. The divergent section D_1 must be designed carefully so that separation does not occur, since this would affect the working section and also cause energy losses, which would have to be allowed for by providing the tunnel with a more powerful (and consequently more expensive) compressor system. The same design criterion applies to the section C_2, whose convergent angle should not exceed 10 degrees.

As in single-throat tunnels, the Mach number variation in the working section is achieved by altering the cross-section of the tube, by means of flexible walls operated by hydraulic jacks.

Supersonic tunnels can be classified according to the method by which they operate, and the way in which the movement of the air is produced. The most common type is the *intermittent tunnel,* in which the movement of air through the working section is induced by the movement of another air supply from a high-pressure level to a low-pressure level. Intermittent tunnels may take the form of an induction tunnel in which compressed air from a storage system is injected part way up a tunnel downstream of the working section, so that dry air from the atmosphere is drawn through the working section; or that of a suction tunnel, which comprises a vacuum storage vessel that is evacuated by means of a suction pump, so that when a quick-action valve is opened in a section leading to the vessel and containing the working section, atmospheric air is sucked into the vacuum creating a high-speed flow through the working section.

Tunnel Corrections

When a test model is positioned in the wind-tunnel working-section, the nature of the air flow around the model is modified by the dimensional limitations of the section. It is therefore necessary to make certain corrections to the aerodynamic coefficients obtained. The coefficient and term most generally corrected are respectively the drag coefficient C_D and the incidence a, so that:

$$a \text{ actual} = a \text{ measured} - \Delta a$$
$$C_D \text{ actual} = C_D \text{ measured} - \Delta C_D$$

where

$$\Delta C_D = 0.125 \, \epsilon \, C_L^2 (S/S_0)$$
$$\Delta a = 0.125 \, \epsilon \, C_L \, (S/S_0)$$

In these expressions S denotes the surface area of the wing, S_0 the area of cross-section of the working section, C_L the lift coefficient and ϵ a coefficient having a value of either plus or minus, depending on whether the tunnel is of the open- or closed-jet type. These corrections remain independent of the Mach number as long as the flow velocity is below the transonic range.

In a supersonic tunnel a system of shock waves forms in front of the model, and these waves are reflected from the tunnel walls in a downstream direction. As long as these reflected shock waves do not interfere with the model, there will be no correction to carry out on the aerodynamic values obtained. Therefore it is necessary to rig and position the model so that while preparing the test run no interference will occur.

Hypersonic Wind Tunnels

We saw in the previous chapter that hypersonic speeds —i.e. those in excess of Mach 5— cannot be studied in conventional wind tunnels, and that special installations are necessary. The fundamental cause of inefficiency in the high Mach number wind tunnel is associated with the extremely large drop in temperature that accompanies expanding flow at these speeds. In the case of air (the working fluid most commonly used in conventional high-speed tunnels), if it is expanded from an ambient temperature to a speed of the order of Mach 4, the final air temperature will be that at which air liquefies. Small tunnels are therefore employed for hypersonic speeds, using a working fluid (such as helium) that has a very low temperature of liquefaction.

The first method used consists of preheating the air before it is injected into the nozzle section. The wind tunnel is usually of the intermittent type and the compressed air is heated in a ceramic heat exchanger, where the temperature may be raised as high as 2,000 degrees C. To avoid excessive heating of the wind-tunnel walls during the injection of this heated air (which might lead to severe oxidation and even melting), they can be constructed with hollow walls, which allow cooling water to circulate. Mach numbers up to 5 can then be obtained.

For higher values of the Mach number, devices known as *shock tubes* are used. These have a long tube closed at each end and divided by a thin diaphragm into two sections; there is a great pressure differential between the fluids in the two sections. The end away from the high-pressure section is used as the test section, so that when the diaphragm ruptures (which may be achieved at a predetermined pressure ratio) a high-speed shock wave travels down the tube toward the test section and thus produces extremely high values of the Mach number for fractions of a second over a model placed at this section. Many hypersonic shock tubes or tunnels are in use; one, at the Arnold Engineering Development Center in the United States can produce a pressure of 14,000 kg/cm^2 by the discharge of a large number of condensers across the reservoir. The high-speed flow thus produced lasts 10 milliseconds; the instantaneous temperature achieved in the shock wave is 17,000 degrees Kelvin. Special electrical pressure transducers have been developed to measure the flow characteristics during this extremely small time interval, and high-speed cameras are used for photographing the shock-wave formation around the model in the test section. The maximum Mach number attained in this shock tube is 15. In other shock tunnels conditions approximating flight at Mach 25 at 100,000 feet and above can be attained.

Another method of carrying out high-speed tests was developed at the American Ames laboratories, where small models were shot from a gun into a low-density gas; Mach numbers as high as 20 were achieved in this way. But a serious disadvantage of this method is the limited range of the model—not to mention the problems of flow and model measurement under these conditions.

Specific Testing

Certain flight forms cannot be simulated in conventional wind tunnels; for instance, the motion known as *spinning*. Therefore special vertical wind tunnels have been built in which models can be put through spins without being fixed to supports. The model is put into the spin at the top of the tunnel, and continues to spin freely while descending into a flow of air moving vertically up the tunnel. In this case calculations concerning the spin are carried out principally by filming the behavior of the model during its fall.

Flutter is also examined under laboratory conditions. When an aircraft is flying at high speed, a speed is reached at which a sustained and often divergent oscillation of the wing or elevator occurs, caused by the interaction of aerodynamic forces, elastic reactions and perhaps inertia. The models used for flutter tests must be dynamically similar to the full-scale surface, and of the same aerodynamic shape. Oscillations are recorded with a small mirror fixed to the moving surface that reflects light from a fixed source, so that the image oscillates at the same rate as the flutter surface. The amplitude of flutter can then be recorded as a function of time.

Free-Flight Trials and Free-Atmosphere Tests

Certain aerodynamic tests are not amenable to wind-tunnel measurements and must therefore be carried out in the normal atmosphere. One method used is to mount the model on a rocket- or jet-engine vehicle that then travels at high speed along a track. This method is used, in transonic experiments, to avoid the errors encountered in wind tunnels due to tunnel-wall interference.

This method of testing is far from new: as early as 1910 the Aerotechnical Institute at Saint-Cyr began to construct a form of railway for aerodynamic experiments; and about the same time, the French engineer Henri Coanda was carrying on tests in which a locomotive pushed a low wagon on which was mounted an aerodynamic balance.

The United States has many high-speed systems; in particular, there is one at Edwards Air Force Base (of the rocket-powered sledge variety) that operates along a railed track about four miles long. In many of these rocket vehicles the high speeds attained make necessary a very powerful braking medium—usually a shallow water course running between the vehicle tracks, so that as the vehicle approaches the end of its test run, a brake surface is lowered into the water and the vehicle is rapidly retarded by the energy loss resulting from the displacement of the water. This takes two or three hundred yards.

Wind-Tunnel Measurements

Wind-tunnel measurements take many forms, because in general they must be sufficiently comprehensive to enable an evaluation of the complete flight details of a particular aircraft, and these vary from air loads exerted upon the aircraft to the temperature and conditions of flow.

PRESSURE MEASUREMENT

The pressures around a test model may be measured by comparing them with the normal atmospheric pressure, by means of a differential alcohol manometer for low pressures, and a mercury manometer for high ones. Measurement of the pressure difference Δp can thus be reduced to reading the height of a liquid in a tube of very small diameter, one that is generally inclined to increase the accuracy of the measurement.

A complete installation thus comprises a series of many parallel tubes connected by flexible tubing to pressure-recording points on the model. These take the form of small holes in the model through which the local pressure is recorded.

To measure the pressure within a stream of fluid, a cylindrical tube with a hemispherical forward part is mounted parallel to the flow direction. Holes pierced in the tube, normal to the flow direction, record the pressure via a differential manometer. This is known as the *static pressure*.

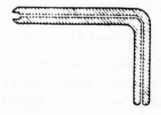

FIG. 39

To measure the total pressure (i.e. that due to the static pressure plus the contribution from the dynamic head, pressure due to the movement of the fluid), an instrument called a *Pitot tube* is used. Invented in 1732 by the French physicist Henri Pitot for measuring the flow of liquids, it consists of a curved tube of very small bore with the open end facing upstream (Fig. 39).

In conditions of supersonic flow, a detached shock wave is formed ahead of the front part of the tube. The pressure given by a direct manometer reading is then that of the pressure behind the shock wave; and as we have already seen, there is a drop in pressure across a shock wave. Therefore to measure the free-stream total pressure, it is necessary to apply a correction to the indicated value.

VELOCITY MEASUREMENT

As we have already seen, it is possible to measure the static pressure and the total pressure (or static plus dynamic pressure). Therefore if we can separate out the term due to the dynamic head, $\frac{1}{2}\rho_0 V_0^2$, we are in a position to calculate the flow velocity. Considering an incompressible fluid, and applying Bernoulli's theorem, then, we have:

$$\Delta p = p - p_0 = \tfrac{1}{2}\rho_0 V_0^2$$

where p is the total pressure, p_0 the static pressure and Δp the dynamic pressure. Having measured Δp, we can see that a knowledge of the value of the density ρ_0 will allow us to calculate the velocity V_0. In the case of supersonic flow (i.e. when the flow cannot be regarded as incompressible) the relationship between the dynamic pressure and the flow velocity is much more complicated.

To measure the local flow velocity at any particular point, and especially flow within the boundary layer, the hot wire anemometer may be used. Its principle is as follows: A metallic filament of platinum or nickel is heated by an electric current of constant value I. At the steady-state condition in a zero-flow velocity, its resistance will be R_0. If the heated element is now subjected to a fluid flowing with a velocity V, cooling of the wire will take place (due to the forced convection process) and the resistance will also fall to a value R. The relationship between the electrical resistance and the flow velocity is determined experimentally—$R = f(V)$—and once the apparatus is thus calibrated, all further velocity measurements are reduced to a measurement of the resistance R, using a Wheatstone bridge. A particular advantage of this hot wire anemometer apparatus is that the small wire used for measurements has only a minute effect on the flow conditions and is therefore ideal for use in the small and sensitive boundary layer.

When we only wish to know the direction of the flow velocity, and not its absolute value (for example, when studying the flow field around a wing), small wool tufts are often stuck to the surface of the model; these align themselves with the local flow direction and thus allow the complete surface to be examined for flow discontinuities. Photographs are taken of the flow field at various speeds so that a complete picture of the flow distribution around the model (and therefore the full-scale aircraft) throughout its speed range can be built up.

MEASUREMENT OF AERODYNAMIC FORCES

The principal use of wind tunnels is to measure forces and moments exerted on test models. For this purpose a system known as an *aerodynamic balance* is used; it measures the three components of force R_x, R_y and R_z and the three components of the resultant moment M_x, M_y and M_z. The type of balance is distinguished by the manner in which the forces and moments are transmitted from the model, by rigid rods or wires.

In supersonic tunnels the model is usually mounted on a sting that fits into the rear of the model in such a position as to assume the position of the wake that would normally be attached to the rear of the model, so that interference is at a minimum. Measurement of forces and moments is largely carried on by such sophisticated techniques as pressure transducers, and results are automatically recorded on punched cards for processing by electronic computers.

The types of balance used in the smaller and simpler tunnels are extremely varied, and we can only mention them here. One of the simplest types consists of three platforms positioned vertically above each other, each with one degree of freedom, and a truncated pyramid at the top that passes through the model's center of gravity, thus creating a moment axis (Fig. 40). For example, the lift platform can only move in the vertical sense. In general, forces applied to the model aerodynamically are indicated by the movement of pointers with electrical recording gear.

Many modern wind tunnels use the technique of *strain gauging*. Strain gauges consist of a very narrow conductor

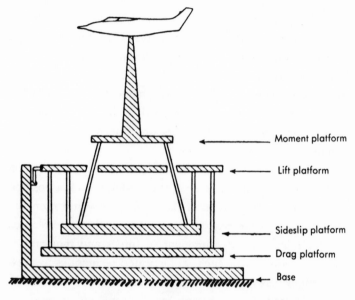

Moment platform

Lift platform

Sideslip platform

Drag platform

Base

FIG. 40

wire attached to the metallic surface of the model at the point at which it is wished to measure surface strain. When the model is loaded and the surface distorted, the strain-gauge wire lengthens, and therefore its electrical resistance is increased. By measuring the change in electrical resistance we can evaluate the loading on the model surface to an accuracy of 1 per cent.

Another system used to measure moments in the low-speed tunnel is the *moment vane*.

For example, suppose we want to measure the pitching

moment of a model aircraft. We mount it between two
points P and P′ at the wing tips (Fig. 41) so that it is free

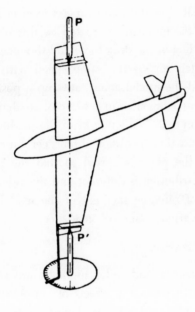

Fig. 41

to oscillate about an axis in the plane of the wing when the
aircraft is in effect free to move in the pitching plane. While
the wind tunnel flow is zero, the model is balanced statically
about the axis PP′ so that the moment about PP′ is zero.
The tunnel is then run at a certain speed so that the model
assumes a balanced position for which the moment about

PP′ is again zero. The value of the incidence for this air velocity is read off on the gauge at the foot of the axis PP′. To determine the pitching moment M, a plate is mounted on the lower part of the balance (its drag having been previously calculated at the tunnel speed used in the preceding test). Thus the moment m created by this plate is known: it is the product of the drag force and the moment arm. The tunnel is then run at the same speed with the plate in position, and the model again takes up a position with the total pitching moment equal to zero, so that at this incidence M + m = 0. The value M of the pitching moment of the model may thus be obtained for a certain incidence. The position of the plate is varied so that the plate pitching moment contribution is different and the value of m varies. The curve of pitching moment of the model can then be plotted for various values of incidence.

FLOW VISUALIZATION

Both modern and older methods are used in wind-tunnel work to study the effects of various flow velocities around a model without introducing probes or other apparatus into the wind-tunnel working section. This is especially important for work in the transonic region and above, where the introduction of even small and well-positioned measuring equipment produces a shock-wave system that materially affects the flow conditions around the model. The first method makes use of the interference properties of light. The *interferometer method* (as it is commonly known) works as follows: By means of a piece of semi-silvered glass with parallel faces, two parallel rays of light are formed that—after reflection from a second piece of glass similar to the first—become superimposed as a single ray (Fig. 42).

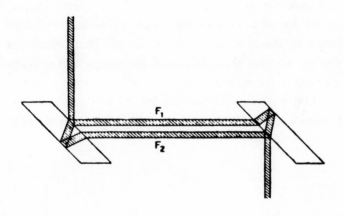

F_{ig}. 42

When the two pieces of glass are absolutely parallel, the light rays cover the same path. But if one of the pieces of glass is rotated about its axis, rectilinear fringes of interference are obtained that are displayed as alternate dark and light rings. If the system is then set up so that it straddles the working section of a tunnel in which air is moving at speed around a test model, the variation of density of the air as the flow changes around the model will show up on the interferometer, because the change in air density also changes the refractive index of the air and therefore alters the optical path between F_1 and F_2. The interference fringes will be displaced by an amount dependent on the change in air density. It is therefore possible to plot the flow characteristics without affecting the flow itself.

The second method (known as the *shadowgraph*) permits examination and photographing of the flow, by projecting the shadow cast by major fluid-density changes (such as shock waves) onto a screen. Thus where the density is higher than the rest of the flow, a darker image appears on the screen.

In a more accurate form, a lens L_1 produces an image S′ from a source S (Fig. 43). If at S′ we place an object of

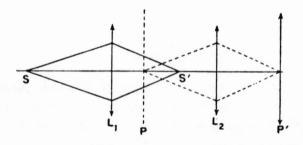

Fig. 43

dimensions exactly similar to the image of S, all the light rays emitted by the source S will be stopped at this position. If a lens L_2 is placed behind S′ so as to give an image P′ from a plane P, this image will not appear as long as the light is stopped at S'. However, if at P the flow around a model is modified in some way, the light emitted by S will be deviated and will provide an image at P'.

The shadowgraph and Schlieren methods are the ones most widely used in the interpretation of supersonic flow fields in wind tunnels.

6 / Aircraft Aerodynamics

Although the wing is the most important part of the aircraft —at least as far as the generation of the lifting force is concerned—all the other components of the aircraft must also be studied aerodynamically, if only to assess their effect on drag, stability, and each other. Furthermore, the general use of the turbojet as a means of propulsion has led to particularly careful study of the design of air intakes for engines, because of the considerable effect this aerodynamic design has on engine (and therefore aircraft) performance.

Streamlined Bodies: Fuselages

The first studies of streamlined bodies go back to the beginning of aviation itself, to the time when dirigibles were in vogue. Early wind-tunnel studies showed that the drag of such a body was at its minimum when the ratio of the length L to the diameter of the midship frame D was about

3. This ratio is known as the *slenderness ratio*. Present-day fuselages have slenderness ratios over 10. The position of the center of force of a streamlined body is unfavorable from the stability point of view, for it causes a pitching moment in the nose-up sense, which in effect increases the fuselage incidence, which in turn causes a higher nose-up pitching moment. This natural fuselage instability is balanced by means of the tail plane.

Interactions

The aerodynamic characteristics of the various parts of an aircraft are influenced by the overall configuration and the relative positions of these parts. In aerodynamic parlance, there is said to be interaction of the forces and moments of the various components that make up the aircraft. The most important of these is the wing-fuselage interaction, which depends on the shape of the fuselage cross-section and the relative position of the wing. From this viewpoint the low wing is least favorable.

In the transonic speed range fuselage design assumes great importance, and a design criterion known as the *area rule* is applied. This rule is based on the following observation: The drag of any body is the same as that of a body of revolution, if the relationship between the two shapes is such that the line describing the shape of the body of revolution in terms of planes perpendicular to the x-axis is the same for the other body. If as a result the optimum form of the body of revolution is determined, that is the shape giving minimum drag in the transonic region. Then, so that the aircraft will have minimum drag in this region, it is designed so that the distribution of the cross-sectional area along the x-axis approximates to the optimum body of revolution. In Figure 44(a) curve I represents the distribution of the cross-sectional area of the body of revolution, while curve II represents the actual area distribution of the interceptor fighter whose planform is shown in Figure 44(b). We can see a number of discontinuities in the interceptor, due to the abrupt change in cross-sectional area at the air intakes, wings and tail unit. To obtain the ideal transonic shape for minimum drag in such an aircraft, the cross-sectional area should be redistributed so that the plot conforms as closely as possible with curve I of Figure 44(a). Using the area rule, the interceptor then takes the form shown in Figure 44(c), with indentations in the fuselage in the vicinity of the wing and tail plane, an increase in fuselage cross-sectional area just behind the wing, and a lengthening of the aircraft's nose.

The area rule has been proved in wind-tunnel tests, and most modern fighters required to operate for any length of time in the transonic region are designed according to this requirement. Convair's F-102 interceptor was one of the first aircraft to be adapted according to the area rule. Originally planned as a subsonic craft, the application of the area rule to the redesign of the second prototype produced an aircraft that achieved supersonic speed on its first flight. Perhaps the most obviously area-ruled aircraft in use today is the Blackburn NA-39 Buccaneer with its "waisted" fuselage.

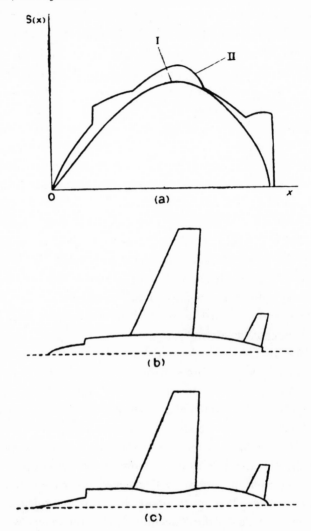

Fig. 44

Other important interactions—which space does not allow us to discuss further here—are those produced between the elevators and wing flow.

Turbojet-Engine Air Intakes

Most modern aircraft are powered by axial-compressor type turbojet engines. These require an enormous quantity of air, so that it is essential that their intakes operate at maximum efficiency. Air intakes in general fall into two principal categories: the Pitot type, which are situated either in the nose of the aircraft or in under-wing pods; and lateral intakes, which are gill-form and are situated on the side of the fuselage. In the Pitot type the air sucked in is normally without any disturbances, while in the lateral type the boundary layer attached to the fuselage can be taken into the intake. Because this layer of air has a low velocity compared with the free-stream flow, it lowers the efficiency of the intake, and steps must therefore be taken to prevent the fuselage boundary layer from entering the engine. Boundary-layer bleeds are therefore provided, in the form of slots on the fuselage wall at the entrance to the intake, and the "dead" air is thereby diverted from the engines back to the fuselage surface at a point further downstream.

A comparative evaluation of the various types of intakes may be carried out by means of the coefficient:

$$C_p = \frac{p_t - p_0}{q_0}$$

in which p_t is the total pressure at a section situated just inside the air intake, p_0 is the static pressure of the undisturbed air, and q_0 is the dynamic pressure. Maximum intake efficiency is obtained when C_p has its highest value.

A particularly interesting example of fuselage air intakes has been developed by the N.A.S.A. This intake is characterized by its complete submersion in the wall of the fuselage. It provides efficiency without boundary layer bleeds, but is unfortunately accompanied by an increase in external drag.

When an aircraft reaches and then exceeds the speed of sound, the intake problem is complicated by the fact that shock waves appear in front of the air intake. The air is compressed as it passes across this shock wave, and its flow direction is turned outward away from the intake centerline. Thus air that would otherwise enter the intake is diverted, so that it becomes of great importance that the intake center body be so positioned that the shock waves angle back to meet the edges of the intake. The layout of the center body intake is shown in Figure 45 with the shock waves well ahead of the intake edges. To achieve maximum intake efficiency at supersonic speeds, it is therefore necessary to move the center body spike so that at each speed the oblique shock waves fulfill the above requirement. The importance of the exact positioning of this center body is demonstrated by the fact that if the center body is too far forward by a few inches, then the displacement of the shock system from the lips of the intake will cause a loss of thrust of about a third.

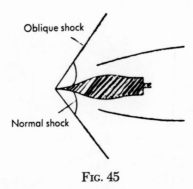

Oblique shock

Normal shock

FIG. 45

Results Relative to the Complete Aircraft

Like the wing, the aircraft can be described aerodynamically by a series of curves such that each curve corresponds to a different flight condition. Furthermore, with each of these is associated a curve of C_m against a that has considerable significance as regards longitudinal stability. If dC_m/da is negative, the aircraft is stable; conversely, if dC_m/da is positive, the aircraft is unstable. In practice this means that an increase in incidence produces a negative pitching moment, according to the conditions established in the section on moments.

If we wish to change the pitching moment coefficient in relation to the incidence, we move the tail plane elevator through a certain angle β. For each elevator angle the pitching angle coefficient is displaced as shown (Fig. 46).

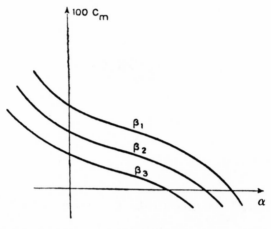

Fig. 46

It is evident that the aircraft's condition of longitudinal equilibrium corresponds to a zero pitching moment, and Figure 46 shows that at a certain incidence the equilibrium position can only be achieved by the deflection of the elevator through a certain angle. A curve of the form $\beta = f(a)$ can then be plotted in which two regimes are evident: one where C_m is greater than 0, and one in which C_m is less than 0 (Fig. 47).

In the same way, if values of C_m and β are chosen for various values of constant incidence, the curves $C_m = f(\beta)$ can be plotted as shown (Fig. 48). The gradient or slope of these curves $dC_m/d\beta$ represent the control efficiency, and

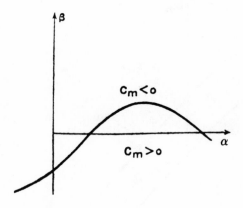

FIG. 47

generally $dC_m/d\beta$ is less than 0. The curve $\beta = f(\alpha)$ represents the aircraft's maneuverability (Fig. 48).

Two somewhat unconventional configurations with interesting aerodynamic characteristics may be noted: the flying wing and the canard type.

The flying wing is, as its name implies, an aircraft without a fuselage; as a result of the drag reduction thus obtained, performance is improved. Unfortunately, serious stability problems arise from the use of this configuration: as there is no tail moment arm in the conventional sense, the design must be inherently stable in itself. In practice this is impossible to achieve, but compromise solutions have been proposed, and some flying-wing aircraft have been built and operated (although with only moderate success). The latest

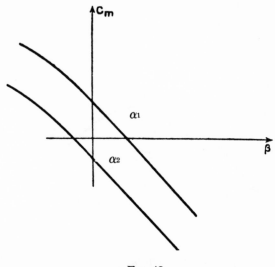

FIG. 48

design proposal for a flying-wing aircraft is that for the laminarized airliner for transatlantic flight suggested by the Handley-Page company.

The canard configuration is particularly interesting. The name means "tail first," or more correctly, that the aircraft has a main wing and a fore plane rather than a tail plane. This configuration was used for many of the very first airplanes, but was then dropped in favor of the rear-mounted plane. However, with the approaching operation of supersonic airliners, the use of the canard configuration to solve some of the stability problems associated with supersonic flight is again being suggested. The use of a fore plane means that the surface is removed from the down-wash of the main wing, and is therefore better able to carry out its design function. However, there is a converse effect, and a downwash effect from the fore plane upon the main wing. Many missiles have a canard configuration.

The Propeller

A propeller is essentially characterized by its axis of rotation and the number of its blades. To define the form of the blades it is sufficient to know the shape of the blade profile of the various sections from root to tip in planes perpendicular to the axis of the blade (Fig. 49). Let us

Blade axis

FIG. 49

consider one such section, situated at a distance r from the axis of the propeller. We can define the chord line of the propeller profile AB as for a wing profile; the angle a that this makes with the plane of the propeller is known as the *blade angle*. The pitch of this section is the pitch H of the geometrical helix whose axis is coincident with the axis of rotation of the propeller and is tangential to the reference chord of the section under consideration. When all sections have the same pitch, the propeller is said to be a *constant pitch unit*. The value of the pitch is given by the expression $H = 2\pi r \, tg \, a$; for the propeller to be of constant pitch, the condition $r tg a = $ constant must be satisfied. If V is the forward speed of the propeller (i.e. the speed of the aircraft) and N the rotational speed in revolutions per second, the resultant speed of the local section is:

$$V_R = \sqrt{V^2 + 4\,\pi^2 r^2 N^2}$$

as shown in Figure 50.

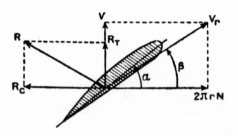

FIG. 50

This speed V_R is in a direction making an angle β with the plane of rotation, and the difference in the angles given by $a - \beta$ is the effective incidence of the section. For a given propeller rotational speed and a given value of a, the effective incidence decreases as the aircraft's forward speed increases.

The velocity of the air in relation to the profile is equal and opposite to V_R. Therefore if we consider a blade element of thickness dr, it is subjected to a resultant aerodynamic force dR, which can be reduced to a component dR_T along the axis of rotation of the propeller and a component dR_c along the plane of the propeller.

The thrust of the blade element is dR_T, which acts in the same direction as the airstream velocity; dR_c is the resistive force the blade element must overcome, which gives a torque $dC = r\, dR_c$. The corresponding power required to drive the propeller section against this force is $dW = 2\pi N\, dC = 2\pi Nr\, dR_c$.

The blade-element efficiency is given by the ratio of thrust power to torque power:

$$\rho = \frac{V\, dR_T}{2\pi Nr\, dR_c}$$

The functioning of the propeller varies with the relative values of the propeller rotational speed and the forward speed of the aircraft. Let us then fix the rotational speed at a value N, and progressively increase V, the forward speed.

When V is zero (i.e. when the propeller is turning in the same plane about a fixed point), dR is almost perpendicular to the tangential speed $2\pi Nr$: when V increases, the resultant pivots forward but can still be vectorized into a thrust force and a resistive torque (Fig. 51(a).

If we continue to increase V, and therefore change the incidence further, there comes a point when the thrust force declines to zero and then changes direction. The aerodynamic resultant can then be broken down into a negative force dR_T that is now a braking force, and the resistive torque dC. This characteristic of the propeller is adopted to

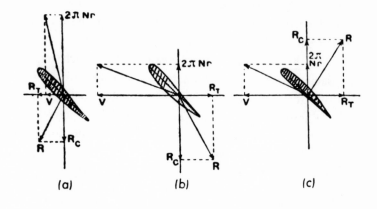

FIG. 51

form an additional method of braking when an aircraft is landing, but in that case the negative thrust force is produced by giving the propeller a negative pitch angle (Fig. 51(b).

Finally, we can define a pitch angle such that the aerodynamic resultant can be vectorized into a negative thrust force and a positive torque dC, which is then a driving torque (Fig. 51(c).

Just as for wings and the other parts of aircraft, we can define non-dimensional coefficients for the propeller that represent the aerodynamic forces.

Calculations by the process known as *dimensional analysis* lead to the following expressions:

For the thrust force: $\mathrm{T} = c_t \rho \mathrm{N}^2 \mathrm{D}^4$

For the power loss: $\mathrm{W} = c_w \rho \mathrm{N}^3 \mathrm{D}^5$

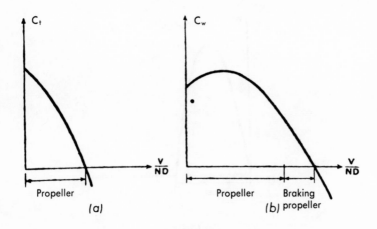

FIG. 52

where ρ represents the density of the air, and c_t and c_w are the thrust and power coefficients respectively.

Figures 52(a) and 52(b) represent the variations of these two coefficients as a function of the parameter V/ND, which is known as the *advance ratio*.

Propeller efficiency is expressed as:

$$\eta = \frac{TV}{W} = \frac{c_t \, V}{c_w \, ND}$$

The form of this relationship between propeller efficiency and advance ratio is shown in Figure 53.

Compressibility of air affects the propeller just as much as it does the wings. Compressibility effects are first experienced at wing tip, since it is here that the resultant air velocity is greatest.

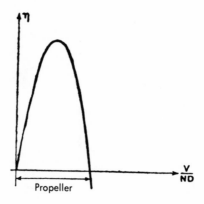

Fig. 53

Wind-tunnel tests have shown that the thrust coefficient increases up to a value of about Mach 0.7 and then decreases, while the power coefficient increases steadily with increasing Mach number. In fact, of course, because of the combined result of forward and rotational speed, the propeller reaches Mach 1 well before the aircraft wing, say at approximately Mach 0.7. The thrust of the propeller then decreases very rapidly (about 10 per cent for every increase in forward speed of 100 feet per second). It has therefore been necessary to adopt high-speed propeller profiles—ones with large chords on the propeller tips—so that at this point, where the compressibility phenomena are first experienced, the propeller profile has a low thickness/chord ratio. Thus propellers with squared tips and of practically rectangular planform have been adopted.

Once the whole of the blade is operating at airflows in the region of Mach 1, a high drag penalty is incurred, especially due to the root sections of the propeller blade. This can be partially remedied by insuring that the root is suitably faired into the propeller hub.

7 / Automobile Aerodynamics

The effect of air flow around a body is not only of importance in aviation, for as the speed of the various types of surface transport increases, these vehicles have to contend with the resistive force or drag associated with movement through the air. Express locomotives that travel at speeds well in excess of 100 m.p.h. are designed so that their aerodynamic profile offers minimal resistance to the air.

The same design care should apply to automobiles, but it is only recently—with the increasing demand for high speeds—that it has become worthwhile to pay particular attention to the aerodynamic streamlining of cars. We can readily see, however, that any reduction in the aerodynamic drag of a car will lead to a reduction in the power required for any given speed, and hence gasoline consumption will be reduced. As we have already seen, though, streamlining generally takes the form of decreasing the thickness/chord ratio (or height to length, for the automobile), and this feature is not always compatible with the qualities of comfort and minimum length for parking and garaging required by the owner. The aerodynamic drag of a car can be simply expressed as $D = a + k V^2$, where a and k are constants and V is the car velocity.

The value of a is approximately constant at all speeds, and depending on the size and design of the car, a is usually larger than the kV^2 term at speeds up to about 40 m.p.h. Since above this speed the second term is dependent on the speed squared, the drag rises comparatively rapidly; and it is here that streamlining becomes important. Although many modern cars have a long, low silhouette that suggests a good aerodynamic design, this is more a question of fashion than a concession to low drag forms. Sports cars and specially designed racing cars do, however, depend on aerodynamic design for their external shape and consequent performance.

The forces acting on a car traveling at speed can, like those on a plane, be broken down into *lift, drag* and *side force* (or *drift*). The lift force on the conventional automobile is practically negligible, although we should note that in cars designed to achieve record-breaking speeds (for example, Donald Campbell's *Bluebird*) it is customary to insure a slight negative lift force, to improve the car's road-holding characteristics. The drift force on a car is not important, except in conditions of high winds blowing at right angles to its direction of travel.

Drag, however, must be considered. Since drag varies

with the square of the speed, and the cruising speeds of even the smaller and lower-powered cars are reaching 60 and 70 m.p.h., it is worth avoiding an abrupt air-flow separation behind the rear window. The art of the automobile aerodynamicist consists essentially of making a successful compromise between the functional requirements of the car and its cost on the one hand, and the reduction of air resistance at high speeds on the other. An examination of the external shapes of cars during the last fifty years shows the following successive changes: fairing the various accessories (such as lights and wheels) into the main body, incorporating bumpers in the general line of the vehicle, shaping the rear of the car, and smoothing all sharp edges.

Furthermore, since the automobile does move in contact with the ground, flow beneath it is also important. On cars with rear-mounted air-cooled engines, the fact that the boundary layer is sucked into the cooling intake reduces external drag.

For comparison, here are some values of corresponding drag coefficients for different cars:

> Citroën 11 ch.................0.65
> Renault 4 ch..................0.42
> Dauphine 0.32
> Dyna-Panhard 0.30

Measuring the Coefficient of Drag

This measuring is done similarly to that used for finding the forces and moments on aircraft, i.e. the vehicle is mounted in a wind tunnel. There is, however, one essential difference between the aircraft and the automobile: the presence of the contact surface, the road. Therefore if realistic results are required from wind-tunnel tests on a car, it is necessary to simulate this surface in the wind tunnel. Similar problems arise with aircraft when they are in proximity to the ground during landing and take-off studies. Two methods are adopted to allow for the road effect in wind-tunnel work: the moving floor, and the "image" method. In the first case the vehicle is placed on a belt that moves along under the vehicle with the same velocity (speed and direction) as the air flow in the tunnel (Fig. 54). This system is rather sensitive and involved. The sec-

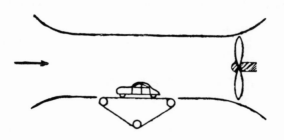

Fig. 54

ond method is used more often: the plane representing the ground is replaced by a second car (or model thereof) symmetrical to the first so that the wheels of the two vehicles touch (Fig. 55). As a result of the system's symmetry,

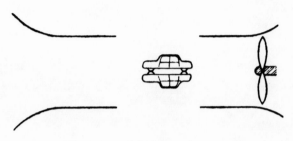

Fig. 55

theoretically no air crosses the imaginary plane between the two vehicles that represent the road. In reality, however, the flow between the two models is more or less turbulent, and vortices are created between them. Results are improved by positioning there a fixed metal plate representing the ground.

Bibliography

Bibliography

BOOKS

Duncan, Thom and Young. *The Mechanics of Fluids*. London: Edward Arnold, Ltd.

"High Speed Aeronautics and Jet Propulsion." This British series (published in this country by Princeton University Press) contains the following titles of particular interest:

Vol. III: Emmons, Howard W. (ed.). *Fundamentals of Gas Dynamics*. 1958.

Vol. IV: Moore, F. K. (ed.). *Theory of Laminar Flows*. In preparation.

Vol. V: Lin, Chia-ch'iao (ed.). *Turbulent Flows and Heat Transfer*. 1959.

Vol. VI: Sears, W. R. (ed.). *General Theory of High-Speed Aerodynamics*. 1954.

Vol. VII: Donovan, A. F., and H. R. Lawrence (eds.). *Aerodynamic Components of Aircraft at High Speeds*.

Vol. VIII: Donovan, A. F., and others (eds.). *High Speed Problems of Aircraft and Experimental Methods.* 1961.

Houghton, E. A., and A. L. Brock. *Aerodynamics for Engineering Students.* New York: St. Martin's Press, 1961.

Rebuffet, P. *Aérodynamique Expérimentale.* Paris: Librairie Beranger.

Thwaites, Bryan (ed.). *Incompressible Aerodynamics.* New York: Oxford University Press, 1960.

PERIODICALS

Aerospace Engineering. Institute of the Aerospace Sciences.

Aircraft Engineering.

Canadian Aeronautical Journal. Canadian Aerospace Institute.

Flight International.

Interavia.

Journal of the Aerospace Sciences. Institute of the Aerospace Sciences.

Journal of the Royal Aeronautical Society.

La Recherche Aéronautique. O.N.E.R.A.

The Physics of Fluids. American Institute of Fluids.

Society of Automotive Engineers Journal.

Index

Index